KEEPING THE FAITH

Keep the faith !

Robyn

Check out these other books by Vanessa Miller

Long Time Coming

Yesterday's Promise

A Love for Tomorrow

A Promise of Forever Love

Former Rain

Abundant Rain

Latter Rain

Rain Storm

Through The Storm

Forsaken

Forgiven

This Far By Faith (editor)

Have a Little Faith (editor)

KEEPING THE FAITH

An anthology edited by

Vanessa Miller

Butterfly Press, LLC
Dayton, Ohio

Published by Butterfly Press, LLC

Butterfly Press
PO Box 26478
Dayton, OH 45426

ISBN 978-0-9728850-7-2

PUBLISHER'S NOTE

Cover Design by Candace K

This anthology is dedicated to my wonderful mother, Patricia Miller Harding; she kept the FAITH until the very end. I'll miss you, mom, but I know we will meet again.

Table of Contents

Introduction

When I began this project, I wanted to help God's people keep the faith even while going through touch situations. Along the way to finishing this project, my sweet mother was diagnosis with kidney cancer which had spread to her liver and lungs. The doctors told us that they wouldn't be able to do anything to save her life because the cancer was in the final stage.

My mother didn't listen to a word those doctors had to say. She believed the God could do the impossible and so did (and do) I. She put her trust in God and remained calm at all times. I never really knew just how strong my mother really was until her final days on this earth. God may not have healed her body, but Patricia Miller Harding has now been rewarded with the wings of angels... because she kept the FAITH!

I miss my mother dearly. My heart aches and I still cry often because of the great loss in my life, but I am not without hope. God is still on the throne and He will see me through.

And this is my prayer for all who read this anthology... when life knocks you down or sends more trouble than you can handle, don't ever stop believing that there is a God in heaven and He is well able to bring you through.

KEEP THE FAITH!

Shattered for a Moment
Regina Crafter

𝒯he school bell rang.

"*Finally!*" I thought to myself as I stood at the blackboard explaining the main concepts in today's lesson. I sighed in relief for my feet as I heard that sound. You would think after twenty three years of teaching, I would be more selective about my choice of shoes. Twenty-nine students to a teacher is a little overwhelming at times, and today was one of those days. I grabbed my AKA sunglasses off my desk, walked my students down the hall and out the front door as quickly as possible. It always amazes me how energized middle school students are at the end of the day. I was drained from today's activities and this was the day that I had to monitor the bus riders.

I walked outside and immediately put on my sunglasses. The sun was set high in the cloudless blue sky, beaming ninety-eight degrees of heat on Quail Valley Middle School's campus in Missouri City, Texas.

The buses that lined up along the curb looked like a long yellow anaconda swallowing each student whole as they entered the doors. Just as the last bus had started to pull off, I heard a few students call my name, "Mrs. Crafter, Mrs. Crafter, have a blessed day."

"You do the same," I yelled back to them.

As the busses pulled out, I turned to go back into the building fanning myself with the folder in my hand. I stopped in the main office to check my mailbox before heading back to my classroom to start grading some papers.

"Hey, Regina, how are you doing?" the secretary, Mrs. Baker asked.

"I'm doing great," I replied as I shuffled through the mail. "And how are you doing?"

"Long day, and it's still not over," she said before she answered the phone. "QVMS, how may I help you?"

The building was almost deserted except for a few remaining students who had after-school activities. I smiled as I strolled passed them and went into my room. I sat down at my desk, grabbed a bottle of water, kicked off my shoes, picked up the stack of test papers from the tray and placed them in front of me to grade. Suddenly, my cell phone rang. I looked at the caller ID and saw that it was my friend, Roderick.

"Hey," I said, "what's up?" As he began relaying some story to me about his son, I placed my reading glasses on the bridge of my nose and reached across my desk for my red grading pen and accidentally brushed up against my chest...and that's when I felt it. I could only guess that it was a natural reaction when I jerked my hand away. I could still hear Roderick talking, but I was lost in the conversation between my heart and mind.

"There is something there," my mind said.

"Impossible!" my heart replied. *"Can't be, I just had a mammogram three months ago, which came back negative."*

"There is something there," my mind repeated.

"But I just ran a half-marathon last year. I am in perfect shape," my mind compromised.

As I sat there dazed and confused, the noise in the hallway made me aware that my door was ajar, so I got up with my cell phone still attached to my ear and closed the door. With my mind focused on the situation at hand, I had no idea what Roderick was saying however, I responded, "Uh huh." I got a piece of

10

construction paper from the file cabinet and taped it to the window of my door.

"Lord I hope there isn't a camera in here like there are in the hallways," I thought as I began to examine myself smack dab in the middle of my classroom.

"Oh my goodness, there is something there," my mind relayed a message of confirmation to my heart as I felt something hard.

Before I knew it, I had cut Roderick off and said, "Roderick, I'm going to have to call you back; I don't know if I am going crazy, but I think I just found a lump in my breast."

At this point, I packed up my things and left work as fast as I could. My greatest desire at this point was fulfilling the need to be home with my family. I was consumed by my thoughts until the cell phone's ring tone shifted my attention. It was my good friend Renee. I immediately told her about the detection.

"Are you sure it's a lump?" she questioned. "You just had your mammogram in July, which came back negative, right?"

"Right."

"Well I know that you are going to have that checked out?"

"Of course I am," I answered, "First thing tomorrow I am calling the doctor."

"I figured you would because you are so adamant about making sure everybody else gets checked. I know that it's probably nothing because you have always been so healthy."

Her words had brought me peace. My mind and heart began to relax from the weight of worry. I had decided that I wouldn't tell my husband, however, I would call the doctor and make an appointment the first chance I got at work the next day.

When I finally arrived home from work, I prayed and ate dinner with my family, helped our son with his homework, graded

11

papers, and did my lesson plans for the following week as if it was any normal day. I tried to suppress worry as long as I could, but as the moon began to announce its arrival, worry eventually reared its ugly head into full view. Before going to bed, I had taken a shower and checked for the lump, unfortunately it was still there.

The next day I was eager for answers and tried to remain calm at work as I watched the clock tick at a snail's pace. Without delay, I called the Sugarland Medical Center and after going through the automated prompting, I had finally gotten through to make an appointment.

A woman with a cheerful voice answered, "Good morning, Sugarland Medical Center, how may I help you?"

"I would like to make an appointment for another mammogram, my name is Regina Crafter," I said.

I could hear her typing on her computer. "Well, Mrs. Crafter, you were here a couple of months ago, and the test results came back negative."

I replied, "Yes ma'am, I know that, but I found a lump yesterday and would like to get another mammogram, please."

She hesitated and then stated, "Mrs. Crafter, your insurance will not cover another visit."

"That's OK," I replied, I'll pay for it."

"All right," she said, "The next appointment I have available is in January."

"January!" I gasped. "Ma'am this is October. I can't wait until then."

"Well, I'm sorry Mrs. Crafter that's the earliest appointment we have available."

After thanking her, I hung up. I had a few minutes left on my break, so I dialed my doctor's office, and explained the situation to the receptionist.

"Well Dr. Steven's is in with a patient, but once he is available I will talk to him about the situation and get back with you."

Fifteen minutes later, the receptionist called to inform me that Dr. Steven's had faxed orders over to Sugarland Medical Center, to setup an appointment within two days."

I exhaled a heavy sigh of relief and said, "Thank you, very much."

Forty-eight hours later, my husband and I walked into Dr. Steven Thomas's office. I focused on the TV mounted on the wall with its messages about eating and living healthily and once again I was reminded of my lifestyle. I have always maintained a healthy lifestyle; from eating to working out religiously. In the middle of those thoughts, I heard "Regina Crafter." It was the nurse calling me. I jumped to my feet and followed her into the examination room.

She asked my husband and me to have a seat. She smiled and opened my folder. "It states here," as she read from my records, "there is no history of breast cancer in your family. And you were recently diagnosed with a cyst two years ago that had been exasperated. Is that correct?"

I nodded, "Yes that's correct." I said to the nurse, "Maybe the fluid may have come back."

The nurse shook her head. "Well, let me reassure you, that isn't the case, because two years ago, that was in your left breast." With that new found information, it felt as though my heart had dropped into my stomach. There was silence before she asked "Have you been consuming a lot of caffeine."

"Not excessive amounts, but I do drink Diet Coke," I answered. "But I have been taking my vitamin E pills."

13

She nodded and wrote the information in the folder. Then she placed the folder on the desk and told me Dr. Steven would be in shortly to proceed with the biopsy. My husband and I were engaged in a conversation when we heard a light knock at the door. Dr. Steven Thomas walked in with a Colgate smile and apologized for being late. He stated that he had an emergency at the hospital. I've always admired Dr. Thomas because of his pleasant bedside manner. He instructed me to lie back on the bed as he began the procedure.

The exam took a little over an hour and a half, mainly because I asked a lot of questions. Once it was over Dr. Thomas and the nurse left me alone with my husband to get dressed. I was deep in thought when a light knock on the door brought me back to reality and Dr. Thomas walked in holding a folder.

"Mr. and Mrs. Crafter," he said, opening the folder," I wanted to let you know that the sample of the tissue that I took was sent to the lab for testing. One of the tests is called a histopathology, which is where we have frozen the tissue and have it examined very closely through a microscopic lens. This process doesn't take that long, so I should be getting the test results back shortly, but the downside of this procedure is that these results aren't 100% accurate.

But," he continued, "I also had them do a full report which takes up to 24 hours, that's because these tests are more thorough which makes the results more accurate."

"What are the chances of me having cancer?" I asked.

"Well," he sighed, putting his pen into his chest pocket. "I don't want to put the cart before the horse, and on a positive note, you had a mammogram only three months ago which came back negative, so let's just hope for the best today and deal with tomorrow's issues tomorrow," he said with a comforting smile. As

14

he walked a couple of steps toward the door, turned around and asked, "Are you training for any upcoming marathons?"

"Yes, I'm trying to get ready for the Houston marathon in January." As my husband and I walked out of the office, I looked at my watch and realized that I had only asked Mr. Winbush to cover two of my classes. I was in the middle of dialing my school when we heard Dr. Thomas's nurse calling us back to the office. Before we could step across the threshold, Dr. Thomas was there with that Colgate smile again. "We just got the test results for the frozen pathology report, and they are negative." My husband and I breathed a huge sigh of relief. "And I believe that the test results from the full report are going to be negative as well, but we won't know until tomorrow. I will give you a call around nine o'clock."

That night I slept better than I had in the past few days. I opened my eyes to the sun shining through my shutters to confirm another new day had arrived. I had high hopes in believing for the best, therefore I had decided not to go to work and wait for the doctor's call. I looked up at the clock and it was just a little after nine when the phone rang. I answered it on the third ring.

"Hello Regina," Dr. Thomas said. "How are you doing today?"

"I'm fine." *"Lord,"* I prayed, *"Don't let me have cancer."*

"We got your test results back," he paused. "I am sorry to inform you that your test has come back positive for Mammary Ductal Carcinoma, which is the most common type of breast cancer in women."

In your case, you have very dense tissues which made it very hard to read on a mammogram. That is probably why it showed negative three months ago.

"I'm sorry," I said calmly. "Could you please repeat what you just said?" After hearing it a second time, I had to take a deep breath to allow the shocking information to sink in. And then I asked, "What do we do next?"

He replied, "First, we are going to run some more tests to see what stage the cancer is in; and then after that, we will take it from there. So we need to get you in here as soon as possible so we can get those other tests run."

I thanked Dr. Thomas for all his help. However, my plan was to go to MD Anderson Cancer Center. He informed me that MD Anderson on average takes at least two months to get an appointment and he advised me that I should not wait that long. It was important to find out what stage the cancer was in. I informed Dr. Thomas that I would get into MD Anderson. Once again I thanked him for his help. He wished me the best and asked me to keep him informed.

After I hung up the phone, I thought, *'How on earth could my life be shattered in a matter of seconds? Not even an hour ago, I was in the middle of my three mile run, thinking what a beautiful morning, listening to the birds chirping, running past the ducks in the lake and enjoying life. I even broke twenty-seven minutes that morning on my three mile run. I was in a zone. Little did I know, that my life was about to change. After one call from a doctor, I'm diagnosed with breast cancer at the age of forty-five; with no history of cancer in my family. How could this happen?'*

I paused and thought to myself, I am a very competitive woman, and I knew that I couldn't wallow in self-pity, so I had decided to roll up my sleeves, and pull out my boxing gloves because I was in for the biggest fight of my life.

On that note, I went to my husband who was in the study, and I stated, "That was Dr. Thomas on the phone. I have cancer."

Those were words, I never thought I would utter. He sat back in his chair and it looked to me as if he was in a trance for a few seconds; but he somehow managed to snap out of the daze. He jumped up from his chair and said, "I'm going to call an old employee who used to work at Missouri City Middle School, she is a cancer survivor who does a lot of work for MD Anderson." I told him not to worry about it, my friend Denise Highsmith and my two sorority sisters had already been in touch with them. MD Anderson Medical Center is the number one cancer center in the world, which meant that they had a very long waiting list and getting in there soon was going to take a miracle. The scripture says in St. Matthews, "Ask and it shall be given, seek and you shall find, knock and the door shall be opened." In less than seventy-two hours, God opened the doors for me at MD Anderson Cancer Center. I received a call from Dr. Daniel Booser's office informing me that I had an appointment within two days. Thank God for His Angels on the ground.

On November 12, 2007, I had my first appointment at MD Anderson Cancer Center. It's funny how I had been in that area, taking my mother to St. Luke's Hospital and never paid close attention to MD Anderson which was right next door. When I first approached the hospital, it looked like a college campus with valet parking you would find at a four star hotel.

My husband and I walked into the Mays building for the first time. This is the building designated for breast cancer patients. We rode the escalator to the second floor and proceeded to the elevator which took us to the fifth floor. As we stepped off the elevator, I looked around this very large area. I was astonished by the number of people I saw. It was like its own world. I was startled to see so many people with cancer. Everybody looked different and I realized that cancer did not discriminate. It crossed all racial, economic, and social barriers.

We finally got to an area that had a nice décor and big comfortable chairs. As I sat there, I continued to study the faces in the room. Some were dazed, confused, wiped out, and surprisingly, most were relaxed and carefree. The man right next to me was reading the Wall Street Journal. The very tall lady across from me was typing away on her laptop and smiling as if she had just landed a mega million dollar deal with a Fortune 500 company. Once again I had found myself staring around the room wondering, *'How on earth could so many people have cancer?'* That's when I realized that I had cancer and I was one of those *people.*

On that note, I jumped up from my comfortable chair and started to walk toward the huge windows with the spectacular view of the Medical Center. It was such a beautiful day! There wasn't a cloud in the sky. I never considered myself as a people watcher, but I enjoyed watching the view before me. People were talking, laughing, eating and enjoying the warm sunny day. Man what I would give to have simple in my life right now. However, I knew my life was anything but simple because in the next twenty minutes or so, I'm going to be sitting across from a doctor. "*Maybe the results were wrong,*" I thought; just as someone barked my name.

That person was a middle-aged woman, five feet two, with a deep voice and a big smile. In another life, this woman must have been a sergeant in the military. "Regina Crafter," she barked, "I'm Dr. Booser's nurse." I remember following her and thinking, *'Wow! This lady is definitely ex- military.'*

She took me into the examination room and asked me a thousand questions about my family history, told me that I would be taking a series of tests over a couple of days, and gave me a book as thick as a photo album that told me everything that could happen to me under chemotherapy. She did her best to make me feel as comfortable as possible and she told me that I was a positive person. She wanted to know if I was always this positive. She gave me papers to sign that stated I could die under chemotherapy. Little did she know that I had just embarked on one of the most depressing conversations of my life. She offered my husband and me a snack and told us the doctor would be in shortly.

Footsteps, a light knock at the door, and in walks a man who reminded me of a politician. "Hi, my name is Dr. Daniel Booser," he said, and reached out a perfectly manicured hand to me. I remember thinking, *'If this guy takes care of his patients as well as he takes care of himself, I'm in great hands.'* He told me he had received several e-mails on my behalf and I thanked him for allowing me to be one of his patients. He then proceeded to ask me questions about the lump I discovered on my right breast and also about my family history. Then he asked me if I had any questions before he started the exam.

I had a good feeling about this doctor. I could see why he was world renowned. I closed my eyes and thanked God for my angels on the ground; Andrea Branch and Karen Baker. One of these ladies worked for Dr. Booser and the other was a patient of his. I thank God again for opening this door because this doctor was not taking any new patients.

After Dr. Booser wrote in my chart, he asked me to lie back so he could examine me. The exam took about twenty minutes. He asked me to get dressed and he would be back in ten minutes. My husband and I were engaged in a conversation about the doctor when we were interrupted by a light knock on the door. He sat down to explain to us that he had to find out what stage the cancer was in. So he had scheduled a CAT scan, PET scan and a Bone scan. Those were words I had only heard on television. That's when I asked him, "Are you sure I have cancer? Do you think you need to run your own tests?" After a pause, he said, "I'm afraid so. Our people looked at your pathology report a couple of days ago."

Dr. Booser handed me three prescriptions; two for pain medicine and another one. I asked him what the third prescription was for and he said a wig. I told him, "Doc, I won't need this one." He said to take it just in case. "I said trust me Doc, I won't need this." He chuckled and said he would see me in a couple of days. Before leaving, I asked if it was okay to workout. He asked me what I had in mind. I told him that I jogged between three and five miles five times a week. He stated that it would be fine but once I started the chemo, I would have to be able to read my body and know when to take it easy because chemo can be draining.

My husband and I left. I felt a great need to be at home in my own environment where I could sit back and think. My mind was definitely on overload. I asked God to give me the strength I needed to fight this battle. In return He told me the battle is not mines, it is His. He said all I needed was the faith of a grain of a mustard seed.

At the crack of dawn the next morning, I brushed my teeth, put on my workout attire and headed out the door for my three mile run. This run was different from all the other runs because I felt the weight of the world on my shoulders. Once again God reminded me that this was not my battle but His, and I needed to step aside. I reminded myself that I would beat cancer and see my son graduate from high school and college. I refused to lose because, *'If God be for me who can be against me.'*

Four hours later I was sitting at my desk while my students took a test, mapping out how I would tell the staff and students that I have cancer. The hardest part was telling my students. I love them so much! It was so hard to tell my son, after losing his grandmother three months earlier and only ten days after his ninth birthday, that I had breast cancer. I still shake when I think about his reaction to the news. And even though these children are not my biological children, I still have a close relationship with all my students. I prayed that when the time came, God would give me the strength to be strong and not break down when I told them.

I didn't work the next day because of my appointment. We left home at 4:30 AM and didn't return until 11:15 PM. I've never been poked so much and had so many tests done in my life. I was tired that evening, so my husband and I stopped at the grocery store to pick up a couple of things. I recognized Mrs. Bonnie, the school data clerk, and her family from afar. As they approached, I remember thinking, 'What a beautiful family!' Mrs. Bonnie smiled and said to her children, "This is Mrs. Regina, the lady we pray for every morning." I was dumbfounded thinking that I didn't know her that well yet she and her family prayed for me every morning. After leaving the store, I was exhausted and ready to go to bed.

The next day when I entered the school building, there were three people waiting at my door with Mrs. Bonnie holding her Bible and leading the way. I knew they meant well, and they wanted to see if they could help. I allowed them into my room, I told them I had cancer but cancer didn't have me, and I wanted to continue to live my life. That was the start of praying in my room which was later called the "Prayer Room."

Later that day I went to MD Anderson to meet with Dr. Booser to discuss my test results. I thought I should be at an early stage because I had just been checked three months prior to this, but with cancer you never know. I was called back once again by the lady known as the Drill Sergeant, later to find out that her name was Mrs. June. She asked, "And how are you Mrs. Crafter?" She said my chemo was set up for later that evening, and Dr. Booser would be in to discuss my test results.

Dr. Booser walks through the door with the brightest smile. He told me he had great news for me. I was in the early stage, my lab work was fine, and I could start chemo that evening. He said that I would have to see a video on chemo. I thought, '*Gosh, I had read everything on chemo, now I have to watch a video WOW!*' Dr. Booser told me I would do Taxol for three months. He said he would see me next week. However, if I had any problems I needed to call him right away.

Chemotherapy was nothing like I expected. Even after seeing the video, it was totally different. Here was a room with a bed, dresser, phone, table, and an armoire with a television. I was given a menu to order whatever foods I wanted. That's when the fun stopped. Just as I was feeling comfortable, a nurse came in to start an IV line, poked me four times before telling me that the IV team was coming to run a line for people with small veins like me.

Physically, the chemo didn't feel all bad. I guess I had expected much worse. Basically being a Health Teacher, I knew the effect chemo had on one's body. I had spent my whole life taking care of my body, never a desire to do drugs, and here I was having poison injected into my body. Don't get me wrong, I understood the need to have chemotherapy to destroy cancer cells, but the idea of poison being injected in my body, did not sit well with me.

This procedure took about four and a half hours and then another hour to get home. Needless to say, it was 10:30 PM before getting back to our home. Before going to bed that night, I decided I would keep a diary, and the first words in my diary were, "Cancer is like a second job." Then I thought about it and realized that cancer is not the second job but the main job and it would take every ounce of strength to get through this. I was in for the biggest fight of my life.

Weeks later as I laid in my bed, I glanced at the big antique clock on the nightstand. It was 3:00 a.m. This was yet another night of less than three hours of sleep, compliments of chemo. I thought, *'Well, at least I'm not having hot flashes tonight and having to change my gown and bed sheets.'* Two hours later, I jumped out of bed, only having two hours of sleep. I had decided that I would not run this morning. I would go to the gym after work. I stepped into the shower as the water soothed my fatigued body. I started to wash my hair that had been cut short over a month ago. I grabbed my shampoo and started washing my hair. I then realized that I was holding a clump of hair the size of a golf ball in my right hand. I looked down and almost passed out from shock. Hair was everywhere. I stepped out of the shower to investigate myself in the mirror. I remember thinking, Halloween was two months ago. I forced myself to focus and then it hit me that I had a prescription for a wig.

At that moment, I had a flashback. I told my doctor when we first met that I would not need a prescription for a wig. Time was ticking away. It was now 5:30 a.m. I had less than two hours left before leaving for work. *Oh, my God*, I thought, *we have almost a thousand students and a hundred and fifty-five staff members in our building. Could I really let them see me like this?* I walked into the kitchen where my husband was preparing breakfast. I told my husband that it was time to get the clippers. I sat in the chair thinking, *what is my son going to think of his Mom with no hair?*

23

And Lord, what will my students think? Middle school aged children can be critical at times. My husband said that I had a nice head and everyone could not do that style. I remember thinking, *Are you kidding me?* When I stood up to look at my reflection in the mirror, I loved what I saw. First, I saw a survivor. Second, I saw a woman with a beautiful complexion. Third, I saw a woman with very high cheekbones; thanks to my grandmother. Finally, I saw a woman who kept her physique in shape; thanks to the time I spent running and going to the gym. I ran to my closet in search for the long earrings I purchased five weeks ago. I remember when I first saw these earrings in Macy's; I knew they would be perfect with a bald head. My husband probably thought I was having a meltdown as I smiled looking for the perfect outfit for work that morning.

I was a woman on a mission. I was no longer worried that I had lost my hair. Inside, I was the same person; maybe even a better person. I was convinced, after looking in the mirror that I didn't need a wig. Someone once said that eighty-five percent of what we worry about is useless. I still cannot believe the reaction that I got from the staff and students. I was walking around thinking I was America's Next Top Model. The staff and students at Quail Valley Middle School are beautiful! After school that day, at least twenty staff members came into my room to pray. That's awesome, considering we are not allowed to pray in public schools. One thing was for sure, hair is definitely overrated!,

Every Wednesday, I continued to go to MD Anderson for my chemotherapy treatment. After a month of Taxol, one of the most frequently used drugs for chemotherapy, I noticed that there was a change in the lump on my right breast. I talked to Dr. Booser about it and he felt that it was the same as it had always been. I told my girlfriend, Renee that the lump felt different in size and

24

texture. After another couple of weeks, I knew for sure that the lump had gotten bigger. I remember telling my husband that something was different. He told me I had one of the best oncologists in the world and if he said that it was the same, it probably was. I told him that I agreed on Dr. Booser being one of the best oncologists in the world but because I had contact with my body, I knew something was different. I shared this information with Dr. Booser and he ordered an ultrasound. During the test I asked the radiologist what was the size of my tumor and she stated that I would have to talk to my doctor. Finally, she gave me some numbers and that's when I came to the startling realization that my tumor had actually grown under chemotherapy.

As I sat in the waiting room, the clock ticked by at a snail's pace. I remember Leroy, one of the nurses at MD Anderson, who from day one befriended me. Leroy was also a cancer patient. It must have been the look he had seen on my face that caused him to come over to comfort me. I remember Mrs. June calling me into the exam room. I must have waited for an hour before Dr. Booser came into the room. I had never waited that long. I remember sighing in relief when I heard those footsteps and the light knock on the door. Instead of taking a seat, he charged right in and told me that he never thought I would be in less than two percent of the population. I said, "And what does that mean?" He took a seat and explained that oncologists don't know why, but less than two percent of the population is resistant to chemotherapy.

Part of me said, 'If I thought that hearing that I had cancer was bad, this was an absolute nightmare, I was hoping to wake up from very soon. He told me that he was preparing for a catheter to be placed in me tomorrow, and he was going to start FAC. I reminded the doctor that he said I was going to do FAC the last three months. FAC had to be done every three weeks. My tumor had almost doubled in size in six weeks with Taxol. I asked him if he thought FAC was going to work for me. He said that we could just hope for the best and see what happens. However, because I was resistant to Taxol, I could very well be resistant to FAC. He stated that he had only had one patient like me that he shared with another doctor. Here I am at MD Anderson, the best Cancer Center in the world with one of the top oncologists in the world, and I'm thinking, not only do I have cancer, but I'm in less than two percent of the population that is resistant to chemotherapy.

I looked at him after a pregnant pause and said, "I have a nine year old son." He said, "I know." That's when I knew I was in trouble. I would have fainted if I had not seen the goodness of the Lord in the land of the living. *"Wait on the Lord, be of good courage, and he will strengthen your heart"* (Psalms 27). I remember thinking, *"Why did I come by myself?"* This was supposed to be a simple treatment and it turned into a nightmare. I called my husband and he came right away. My cell phone kept going off but I never answered it. It continued to ring. Finally I answered and it was Renee, who was at MD Anderson looking for me. I couldn't remember why she was there but I had spoken with her while I was in the waiting room and told her my tumor was almost doubled. She was concerned.

Through the whole ordeal, I had been strong. I held my head up and kept going. But that night, I asked God for permission to cry and for the first time, I cried long and hard. I called my girl, CJ and told her that I didn't want to put my family through the burden of what I had just gone through with my mother. She stated that we were not planning a funeral but we were planning a party. I told her plenty of people pre-arrange their funeral. She said, "Good, this is one we are not going to pre-arrange." She said that we could plan a trip and she asked me where I wanted to go.

26

Cynthia (CJ) was my best friend growing up. During college, we lost contact with each other. Luckily, we reconnected about three months ago, and we have been talking every since. She is also a breast cancer survivor. That night in our bedroom I shared the bad news with my husband. We got on our knees and prayed together. I had decided my husband and I would talk to Dr. Booser tomorrow. We walked in and thanked Dr. Booser for seeing us and I got straight to the point. I asked him if there was anywhere on earth where research was being conducted for people like me. I was willing to go to Europe, Africa, it didn't matter. I just wanted to live. He stated that oncologists had discontinued the study in 2004 because they didn't know what to do with people resistant to chemo. He told me that he would try FAC which is usually stronger than Taxol and used every three weeks. I told him I wanted FAC every two weeks versus three weeks. He stated that it is normally done on a three weeks cycle. I told him that "I had a nine year old son who needed me and next to killing me, you do what you have to do!" I wanted treatment every two weeks. I wept that night because the Bible says that, *'Weeping may endure for a night but joy comes in the morning (Psalms 30).'*

The next morning I got down on my knees asked God for forgiveness and told Him I did not doubt Him. I didn't know if I had six more days or not, but I asked God for forty more years.

I finally called my friend, Karen. I had my reasons for not telling her that I had fallen into the less than two percent of the population that was resistant to chemotherapy. Karen was also dealing with her good friend, Mrs. Bonner, who had colon cancer. It seemed as though so many of Karen's friends were being diagnosed with cancer. I asked Karen if she would go with me to my next appointment. Two days later we walked into MD Anderson Hospital hoping for the best. I sat on the bed in the examination room with my eyes closed. I continued to repeat, '*I will live and not die, and declare the works of the Lord.*' Loud footsteps broke my trance. Dr. Booser walked in and I introduced him to my friend, Karen. I told him that I was sure that my tumor had gone down, but then I thought back to my last visit when my expectations were high and my hopes had been dashed. The doctor smiled and said, "In that case, let's take a look right away." The doctor examined me and confirmed that the tumor had gotten smaller; however, he wanted me to have an MRI in about a week. I dropped to my knees and thanked God. I began to cry, but they were tears of joy!

Once again I thanked God for allowing me to have such a personal connection with Dr. Booser. This doctor was becoming more like family to me every day. I think we managed to put on our best poker faces and never gave up hope in the midst of the storm. We were both blindsided by the fact that I was an early stage that ended up being resistant to chemotherapy and we both knew that time was running out because my tumor was growing at a dangerous pace. If FAC did not work for me, then there was only one other drug which happened to be experimental. It had only been out for six weeks.

It was the Friday before Spring Break. I was geared up for my Chemo/Pajama Party that was being held in the Galleria area. I was excited about seeing my dear friends who had prayed for me and supported me during the most difficult times of my life. I looked at my cell phone and the caller ID indicated that it was MD Anderson Hospital. The lady on the other end of the phone said, "This is Lynne. Can you talk?" I stated that I could always talk to MD Anderson. Then she replied, "Are you sitting down?" I asked, "Should I be?" She commented, "Yes." She told me that my tumor had disappeared and that there was no evidence on the MRI that showed any signs of a mass. I yelled out, "Thank you, Jesus!" and that is when I heard clapping and shouting. It reminded me that I still had kids in my class. Several teachers raced into my room to make sure that everything was alright. Talking about a way to start your spring break, here I was with no sign of cancer. As many have given to me, I have tried to model the perseverance of those of us who have struggled to overcome cancer. I hope that my openness will help to generate a network of empathy and awareness that will serve God's plan. I have no doubt that it was my faith that brought me through. From the very beginning of being diagnosed with cancer, I was **Shattered, but only for a Moment!**

Regina Crafter is a graduate of Prairie View A & M University with a B.S. degree in health education. She has an M.S. degree in educational administration. She is a proud member of Alpha Kappa Alpha Sorority. Regina is a devoted mother and dedicated teacher. Need email and website address if applicable

Regina Crafters accomplishments include:

*Who's Who Among America's Teachers 2005
*Lake Olympia Middle School Teacher of the Year 1998
*District Finalist of Secondary Teacher of the Year 1998

*Texas Medical Association Excellence in Science Teaching Award Finalist 2003-2004

*Coordinator for the American Diabetes Association—Raised a total of $ 10,014.25, making Quail Valley Middle School the top middle school in the nation in 2005 to 2006.

*Selected as one of five teachers in the nation to train teachers from around the world on how to run successful campaigns at a Community Leadership Conference in Chicago in 2005.

*Coordinator for Quail Valley Middle School Breast Cancer Awareness Fundraiser. In a three year span, we have raised a total of over $40,000.00 for MD Anderson Cancer Center. Special thanks to ex-NFL players, Keith Byars and Bubba McDowell for their help over the years with various fundraisers.

Regina is a member of Lakewood Church. As the author of my first anthology, I felt like a woman on a mission to tell my story, *SHATTERED FOR A MOMENT*. I am currently writing my first book, *SURVIVOR FROM DAY ONE*, that will give more in-depth information about my life. May God bless you!

If I should die before I wake
Pat Simmons

Now I lay me down to sleep. I pray the Lord my soul to keep. If I should die before I wake, I pray the Lord my soul to take.

It's a simple eighteenth century child's prayer that has been revised by parents throughout the years. It rolls off our tongues without much thought. Then on the morning of July 1, 2005, it became more than idle words.

This is my family's eye witness account what happened to me:

About five in the morning, my husband, Kerry, got up to use the bathroom, then returned to bed. After peering at the clock on the nightstand, he sighed and relaxed. "Thirty more minutes." Not long after closing his eyes, my body shook the bed uncontrollably.

"Pat, wake up." Kerry nudged me a few times.

Not alarmed, his initial thoughts were "the witch was riding me again," a phrase sometimes used to describe sleep paralysis where a person is asleep, but there is still a level of awareness. Sleep experts say it's a natural response to keep us from acting out our dreams. Attempts to move a limb is thwarted until a sudden jerk like a finger or toe wiggling releases the freeze on the body. When I didn't respond or stop, he panicked.

"Jared, Simi," he yelled down the hall to where their rooms were, never leaving my bedside. "I can't get your momma to wake up. Call 911. I think she's in a coma." Fear crept up his spine.

Simi—short for Simone—was sixteen years old at the time. Racing into our bedroom, she cradled me in her arms while Kerry dressed and waited for the ambulance. No one remembered who placed the first 911 call.

"I think she's having a seizure, Dad," Simi guessed at my condition. Maybe she had seen an episode of Grey's Anatomy. I doubt if she learned about seizures in her high school classes. Plus, nobody in my family suffered with them, so she had no point of reference. Kerry wasn't buying her diagnosis as my eyes rolled back and I involuntarily released body fluids. To him, I was dying.

The commotion had startled my son who was then twenty years old. Jared can sleep through anything. His head had probably just dented a pillow an hour earlier, after he arrived home from his overnight shift at UPS.

Jared hurried out of his room and approached the master bedroom, but refused to cross the threshold. He stared at his dad who was now holding me. But Jared didn't want to see me like that. He became delirious as he ran up and down the stairs aimlessly. Jared placed frantic calls to 911, shouting and demanding that they hurry up.

Somewhere between the paramedics getting to the house and Jared "losing it" during a time of crisis as Simi described it, she ran downstairs and grabbed our bottle of holy oil. Believing in the power of the Holy Ghost, she anointed my head and prayed. When the paramedics came into our bedroom, they asked my family my name and then called out to me. My eyes opened and closed again.

"Is she a diabetic?" one of the medical team asked Kerry.

"No."

They advised my husband that I had probably suffered a seizure. They called my name again and in a semi-conscious state,

I responded enough for them to guide me to a waiting stretcher. I don't remember getting on the stretcher or being loaded inside the ambulance. I do recall seeing my neighbor across the street looking at our house. But that's all I remember.

In the ambulance, Jared rode upfront with the driver. Kerry and Simi trailed in one of our vehicles. My husband said the ambulance exceeded speeds of eighty-five miles per hour with its siren blaring. Kerry panicked when he couldn't keep up.

"What's going on? What's wrong?" Kerry called our son on his cell phone.

Jared must have checked with the paramedics. "Nothing, Dad. They're just trying to get Momma to the hospital."

In the back of the ambulance, I woke. Lying on my back, I looked up into the face of a woman who wasn't in my bedroom the night before. She was staring down at me and inserting a needle into my vein.

"Your family said you weren't responding. You're in an ambulance."

I blinked as my heart sunk. *Huh? Did I die and didn't know?* What was she talking about? I'm fine, I thought. All these questions raced through my mind as I remembered the events of the previous night... sewing, washing, and packing clothes for a family trip. I recalled reading my Bible and praying before climbing into bed, then rubbing the peach fuzz on my husband's head just to irritate him. Yep, I was fine.

"I've never been in an ambulance before," I calmly informed the woman as I glanced around. "I've got a hair appointment." It wasn't a joke. I didn't know the severity of what had happened.

"You won't be getting your hair done today," she said matter-of-factly.

Too tired to argue, I closed my eyes and dozed off.

When I woke again, the paramedics opened the back door of the ambulance and pulled me out. The first person I recognized was my son. His stricken expression was startling.

Frowning and clutching an overnight bag over his shoulder, Jared's first words were accusatory, "Momma, what you do that for?"

My poor twenty year old who seemed to revert to a six year old, acted as if I had staged the event to scare everybody. I don't remember my response, but I think Jared had to accept that parents do die and they don't have to be old, gray, and in a wheel chair before they go.

Anguish draped my husband's tear streaked face as he came into the examination room. Panicking, I lifted my arms toward him.

"What's wrong?" Not realizing that I was what was wrong. I had never seen my husband cry. The sight frightened me. I knew we loved each other, but I felt the depth of his fear. He thought he had lost me.

My mother arrived at the hospital. She was a force to be reckoned with in the examination room. Johnnie Cole put fear into the attending nurse. Momma let the woman know there would be no rules that she would follow. "Pat is my daughter and if I want to come in here, I will." The nurse's bedside manner improved dramatically.

Since I couldn't gauge time, I had no idea how long we had been waiting. Soon, a staff neurologist walked into my room. "You didn't have a stroke, a blood clot, or an aneurysm," he advised. "We," referring to his team of medical professionals, "don't know what caused your seizure, but you can go home."

His last words prompted my full attention. Instantly, I was in my right mind. Whatever my husband was about to say, I beat him to it. "I don't think so. If you don't know what caused me to have a seizure then, I'm not going home."

I don't know if it was the look I gave him or the scowl on my mother/bodyguard nearby, but he caved in with a nod. I was admitted to the cardiology wing so they could monitor my heart. After I got settled into my room, a nurse lifted the side rails on my hospital bed.

"For your safety in case of another seizure," she explained.

It proved to be a smart move because later that night, I had another one in my hospital bed. This time I remember the sensation of drooling. The next morning, I inquired to the nurse.

She verified it. "How did you know?"

"I remember I was about to wipe my mouth and my head tilted to my left."

"Then the seizure was on the right side of your brain," she stated matter-of-factly.

When my husband called the room before coming to see me, I gave him the disappointing news about another seizure. Again, we both agreed and informed the doctor that I wasn't leaving until I was seizure free.

Finally, a few days later I was released. The out pouring of calls and visits was humbling. At first, I didn't really question God as I explained to my mother-in-law over the phone. "Who am I that I'm not supposed to suffer? Even as a saint of God, I know I have to go through just like Jesus suffered. It's my season for a trial." Although my conversation with her was private, the devil was eavesdropping and planning an attack.

My family was closed-mouth about describing what happened. Kerry reluctantly opened up to me. "I thought you were

35

dying, brain dead," he confessed. "Your breathing had a haunting raspy sound. In slow motion, it seemed like life was being sucked out of you."

Jared explained, "I woke up when I heard daddy crying. I've never heard him crying in all of my twenty years. You looked like you were dead, Momma."

What stayed in Simi's mind was the scene of my husband and son hugging after the paramedics arrived and they were able to get some kind of response out of me.

Witnessing the seizure was my family's trial, the aftermath began mine. It seemed as if I was becoming anxious, constantly worrying if I was on the verge of having another unexplained seizure. Under Missouri's law, epileptics are forbidden from driving for six months. Some states have driving restrictions up to one year. Bumming rides became exhausting. However, in hindsight, I praise God for those restrictions. On the morning of my seizure, I would have been behind the wheel of my car, driving my daughter and myself to the hair salon. One of us, or both, could have been killed or been critically injured.

Another drastic limitation was no overnight shifts. I had worked eleven at night to eight in the morning for years in a newsroom alone, monitoring scanners. My shift had recently changed from overnight. Otherwise, I would have been at work by myself and not found for possibly hours. A week or so after I returned to work, I noticed that when talking to coworkers, I would at times be in the middle of a thought, that I couldn't complete. It was as if my brain couldn't connect.

I had to stop taking long, hot soaks in the tub or swimming without supervision. I had become one of millions of epileptics who doctors recommended wear a medical bracelet to alert bystanders of what was taking place if I were to collapse, my eyes roll back into my head and I start gnawing my teeth. I couldn't wait for my first follow up appointment. My questions were unrelenting to the doctor. "Since epilepsy isn't part of my family history, what could have contributed to the seizure: lifestyle, medications, past illnesses, and work load?" It was a question that five years later, I have no answer to.

"No, sometimes we never find a cause," the female neurologist responded.

"What!" Somebody is going to tell me something. With no provocation on my part and out of no where, I experienced a major seizure. This was unacceptable, so I began my quest of finding a neurologist who could give me some insight on what could have brought on a seizure from out of no where.

A third neurologist questioned whether my hundred and six degree fever four months earlier played a part in my seizure. "A spinal tap should have been done," he said, almost to himself.

I don't know what caused my high temperature, but that was the sickest I had ever been. The glands in my throat were so swollen that they were bulging. I was too sick to go into my doctor's office. When I finally went to the emergency room, Tylenol had temporarily reduced my fever. Unfortunately almost six months later after numerous tests: Caratoid Duplex, MRIs and Cat Scans for a stroke, brain tumors, or aneurysm... no cause could be detected.

During those months, I also was a guinea pig for medicines and suffered through a few side effects. The fourth medicine, Zonegran, prescribed for control and prevention of my tonic-clonic (previously called Grand Mal) seizures proved almost deadly.

37

The timing couldn't have been worse, within a month of taking Zonegran, my husband was hospitalized. He needed emergency surgery for a gangrene-infected gall bladder. He landed in the same hospital room I had been in months earlier—eerie, huh? Since I couldn't drive, I bummed rides to and from the hospital, worrying about Kerry's first-ever surgery.

I didn't think much of my sleepless nights (a prerequisite for seizures) and agitation. I thought it was a result of Kerry being hospitalized for more than a week. Nine days later, he was discharged. As he laid in our bed, recovering, one serious side effect on Zonegran kicked in.

As a television assignment editor at the time, it was routine to watch the nightly news. So not to disturb my husband, I went into my daughter's bedroom. As I sat on the floor, a creepy feeling started to overpower me. My mind seemed to be telling me to slam myself against the wall. The feeling didn't subside as I ignored the urge and continued to watch the news. As a matter of fact, the enticement to fling myself out the second floor window was overwhelming. Something was wrong. I knew that if I yielded to whatever was commanding me to set something in motion, I wouldn't be able to control it and my demise would be sure.

With deliberate movements, I stood and concentrated on walking to our bedroom. One wrong move and I couldn't be responsible for my next action. My husband glanced from the television to me.

"Kerry, I'm freaking out," I said softly.

He looked at me strangely because I spoke calmly and appeared normal. "Okay."

Trying not to agitate myself, I repeated in a controlled manner. "I'm telling you, I'm freaking out."

Scooting up to the best of his ability, he frowned and gave me his full attention. "What do you mean?"

When I explained the sensation I just experienced, his brows knitted in concern. "C'mon, get in bed. Maybe you'll feel better in the morning."

Yeah right. I had to make it through the night to make it to the morning. Careful of my movements, I did as he suggested and got in the bed. My body still wanted to leap up. I was afraid. Something was happening to me and only God could help me.

Praise God, I woke up the next morning. Again, the children's prayer came to my mind, but the scare wasn't over. I wondered if somehow the medicine was linked to the episode the previous night. If so, I dreaded a repeat experience and it was close to the time for me to take another dose. I googled the drug and its side effects, then called our insurance-sponsored nurse hotline. Not only did the nurse tell me the unusual thoughts were suicidal, but advised me that if I didn't take my next dose I could endure a stat epileptic seizure and never regain conscious. What a choice? I can watch myself self-destruct or unconsciously kill myself.

I did take that medicine until the doctor was able to wean me off and start me on another one. That process took more than a week and during that time, the sensation did return, but since I had identified the culprit and knew I wrestled not with flesh and blood as warned in Ephesians six, I relied on all the strength God gave me to overcome.

Five years later and no more episodes, I remain on medication and patiently wait for a word from God concerning my dormant condition. Jesus once spoke to me years ago concerning excruciating migraines that often left me incapacitated. "I'm going to heal you and you won't even know it." His word did not return void, but manifested itself as He had said.

I do not take one day of my life for granted. James 4:13-15: *You who say, today or tomorrow we will go into such and such a city and spend a year there and carry on our business and make money. Yet you do not know about what may happen tomorrow. What is the nature of your life? You are but a wisp of vapor that is visible for a little while and then disappears. You ought instead to say, if the Lord is willing, we shall live and we shall do this or that.* AMEN.

***Some seizure triggers: failure to take medication as prescribed; lack of sleep increases the frequency of seizures; withdrawal from alcohol, illegal drugs especially cocaine; extreme stress; hormonal changes during monthly cycles or menopausal. For more information on epilepsy go to: www.cureepilepsy.org

Pat Simmons is the award-winning author of *Talk to Me,* ranked #14 of Top Books in 2008 that Changed Lives by *Black Pearls Magazine*; she also received the Katherine D. Jones Award for Grace and Humility from the Romance Slam Jam committee in 2008. Pat is best known for her Guilty series: Guilty of Love, Not Guilty of Love, and *Still Guilty.* Her next work, *Crowning Glory,* is scheduled for release in 2011.

To contact Pat go to: www.patsimmons.net

On My Way to Where I've Never Been
Patricia A. Bridewell

Year - 1984

A jolt of pain slammed me against the shower wall, nearly pushing me ten feet under. When it ended, I rinsed off body wash, wrapped with a towel, and planted my feet onto the cold bathroom tile. I waddled to the bedroom and dialed my OB-GYN physician's message center. Five minutes later, an on-call physician's laughter echoed through the phone as he bellowed, "Its false labor. Call me back when the pains are five minutes apart." His acrid tone made my skin crawl. The last thing I wanted to hear was a smart-mouthed doctor telling me something I knew wasn't true.

"No, I don't think so. This pain is different."

In the back of our Honda Accord, doubled over in the worst pain I'd ever felt in my life, I moaned and changed positions about a hundred times. My husband zoomed down the streets like a mad man on a mission to destroy anything in his pathway.

A frown crossed his licorice-colored face. "Baby, you all right?"

I shook my head and grasped the door handle. "No! Keep driving, but slow down or we're not gonna make it.'"

"We'll get there."

A few cleansing breathes and pursed lipped breathing helped me wade through the next horror. Two minutes and it ended, three minutes later the roller coaster shifted to full gear and with my legs spread apart, I bent my head—sucked in a deep breath and exhaled.

An attendant wheeled me to the registration window while my husband parked the car. Why did I get the slowest registration clerk on the planet? As I stood to transfer to a wheelchair; a gush of water splattered the floor. The nurse beside me gasped.

"Oh, no. . . somebody get a gurney now! Don't move." The scrawny young nurse held my arm until two more nurses arrived.

I gazed toward the wheelchair that floated in a pool of bright red blood, my heart thumped and head spun. I clutched my stomach through another repulsive pain. The rest was like a nightmare I wanted to forget. Frightened by all the beeps of monitors, blood draws, and staff members hovering over me, I squeezed my husband's hand. A tear trickled down his cheek for the first time during our ten years together; I turned my head while he brushed the offending cheek with his hand. My doctor arrived at the hospital within an hour of my admission. After examining me, she left the room and returned a short time later.

Dr. Kerry sat beside me and rubbed my arm. "We've confirmed there's no heartbeat. I think the baby is dead."

"How?" They keep saying the baby is dead, but I felt kicks. This baby's gotta be alive." I grabbed the bed rails and shifted to my side.

My husband, Artis, ran his hand through his hair. "Doctor, this baby can't be dead. I mean, .Patrice said the baby was moving earlier. What could've happened?"

Her brows gathered as she folded her slender arms. "I don't know yet, but I'll find out. Mrs. Baylor had a normal pregnancy without complications." She sighed. "I'm so sorry, but we couldn't detect a heart beat or any viable signs of life."

I tried to remain stoic, but another pain stymied that plan. I raised myself to an upright position, kicked, screamed, cried,—

none of the things we'd been taught in Lamaze classes. Artis put his arms around my shoulders, I shrugged them away.

I panted through dry lips while he tried to feed me ice chips. "Please. . . just. . . leave me alone."

He tried to console me, but the intensity of my labor tore him to pieces. So there I was—alone to face the stillness of a cold room dressed with white walls, spotless floors, and the scent of alcohol. Artis stood from afar watching me and checking in every so often.

On Easter morning at 3:32 a.m., our son Travis Andre Baylor entered the world without a cry or a breath. The nurse brought our eight pound, two ounce baby to me swaddled in a yellow blanket. I cuddled him in my arms, pressed kisses on his forehead, smoothed back a head full of coal black hair, and pulled him to my breast. I wept and shouted "Lord, why? I just want to know why? You could've saved him."

Twenty minutes later a nurse whisked him away, leaving us bemused over the loss of our child. Our world raveled up tighter than a ball of yarn. Before I went home, nurses transfused two pints of blood and I stayed in the hospital for six days. Artis had become so depressed over the ordeal that I thought they'd admit him, too. Although the burden of our tragic loss weighed him down, he never confessed that he was unable to fully recover. We both had sons from previous marriages. My son Darius was twelve and his son Marcus, the same age. We both desperately wanted a little girl, but a healthy baby would've sufficed.

Two years later. Our relationship had melted down faster than ice cubes on a sultry day. Artis had secluded into his own safe little world, ignoring me and the kids as if we were invisible. I kept busy working and entertaining my son, and Marcus, when he visited. Our family whittled down to dissected pieces of a puzzle, and whether or not I could put them back together was the big question. We missed Artis.

"I'm not going to the movies," Artis said, scrunching up his face.

"But I promised the boys pizza and a movie tonight."

"Well, rent a movie, Patrice! We can take them next time."

He pushed a hand mirror in front of his face and patted every hair in place. He shaved, trimmed his moustache, and doused in a well of Pierre Cardin. Dark as the ace of spades, his skin and high cheek bones complimented an unusual pair of hazel green-tinged eyes. His eyes caught everybody's attention—especially women. On the night we met, I was out with girlfriends at a nightclub during my partying days. Artis entered the club and cast his gaze toward me, then stared me up and down. The magnetism in his eyes instantly drew me to him, and that night was the beginning of something more flavorful than a hot shot of Expresso.

"Artis, it's not fair. Why can't you spend one night with me and the kids?"

"Told you Derrick's picking me up and we're hanging out. I deserve a little free time. Okay?"

Free time? Every time I asked him to go somewhere with me he needed free time. His cousin Derrick signed with an NFL football team on the west coast and moved back to Los Angeles. Since then, they'd become inseparable. My only visit to Derrick's Baldwin Hills home was for his birthday party several years ago. New in my commitment to Christ, I knew that socializing with finger-popping, toe-tapping, liquor guzzling folks would've led to an open door of temptation. Had I cornered one of them alone that night, maybe I could've witnessed about Christ. But if I'd tried to witness to a party group, all of them would've scattered faster than flies.

"You know. . .since Derrick has been back, we don't see you on weekends anymore."

"Now, there you go. What you want me to do, tell him I'm not going?" He glanced at his watch.

Artis played that scene out well. He knew I'd never ask him not to go out, and he'd never cancel with Derrick anyway. I remembered the spine-chilling stories he'd told me about him and Derrick dating every woman they could pick up while Derrick was in college. I heard they had more skirts running in and out of Derrick's dorm room than Prince and Usher had in their stadium concerts. No, I didn't want him hanging around that player—and a professional athlete at that.

I shook my head and raised my palm. "Go with your cousin. The boys and I will fix popcorn and watch movies."

My mouth swelled with fury. What could be so important that he would sever his relationship with his family? Artis claimed that Derrick had a girlfriend, but if so, she must be sitting around twiddling her fingers on Saturday nights or dating a side-kick. If I didn't know better, I'd think Artis and Derrick were dating one another. And I needed to talk to Artis about his money spending binges lately.

A restless night ended with a plunge into the Land of Nod. I heard scraping sounds, rubbed my eyes, and turned the alarm clock toward me… it was 2:35 a.m. That racket had to stop if I planned to make Sunday service this morning. I tied my robe, trailed a glow of light from the kitchen, and found Artis sitting at the table with his back turned. I loomed over his shoulder while his eyes fixed on the project before him. He glanced up and almost fell from the chair.

"Girl, you scared me. What you doing up so late, anyway?" He rolled up a white powdery substance in foil and stuffed it and a pipe inside a plastic bag.

"You woke me up, and what's in the bag?"

"Nothin'. Go back to bed." He swooped up his goods and sprinted toward the bedroom; I shadowed his every step."

"Artis Baylor, I know you're not using drugs in this house."

He stopped dead in his tracks and faced me toe-to-toe. "And what if I am?" He shot fire my way through a squinted glare. I'd never seen that look, and it made me uncomfortable. Two steps backward eased his hot breath off my face.

"You can't. Not in *this* house!"

Artis got even more brazen, he thrust his chest forward. "What you gon' do about it?"

Lord, this can't be the same man I married. He's got to be a clone or a twin who'd eased out of hibernation. In all the years we'd been together, Artis had never disrespected me in this manner. He wasn't perfect and he definitely had a way with words when he got angry, but this behavior was different. A rational answer needed to fall out of my mouth soon. Anything.

Artis' voice leaped ten octaves higher. "*I said,* What you gon' do about it?"

I raised my head to face this six feet two inch stranger. "You have two minutes to get that stuff outta my house."

After I checked on the kids, I rushed back to our bedroom and slammed the door.

Artis was no longer in our bedroom. Filled with trepidation over what I'd just done, my hands trembled. I closed my eyes to regain my composure before I slithered into bed. I lay in the bed

46

for over an hour, waiting for him to creep into the bedroom with an apology or a lie. Keys jingled—the front door closed, my nerves calmed

Night progressed to dawn; I woke up alone in my bed. I went through the regular motions of showering and fixing breakfast, but my soul ached. How long had he been in this self-destructive mode without me knowing, and why hadn't I picked up on it? Obviously he didn't care that I knew. When I envisioned the kids standing in the hallway watching Artis smoke crack, blood rushed to my temples. I shoved open the sliding closet door so hard it jumped the track. I sifted through everything in the closet and emptied his dresser drawers in search of drugs. After I finished, I threw his clothes into a duffle bag piece by piece until exhaustion forced me to stop.

On my knees, I cried out "Lord, why? I want to understand why?" I buried my face inside my hands.

Darius tapped on the door "Mom, we're gonna be late."

I smeared tears across my face. "Be ready in a few minutes, honey." I shook my head. Funny how much Darius was like me when it came to punctuality. For years he'd heard me constantly stay on his step dad's case about being on time.

I heaved out several hard breathes, surveyed the mess around me, then placed all of Artis' clothes back in the closet and drawers before I finished dressing. I applied makeup to puffy eyes, tousled my shoulder-length auburn hair, and twirled in the mirror for the third time. My navy suit fit perfect and the matching pearl earrings and necklace topped it off.

I sauntered into the sanctuary with my head held high, giving my Lord and Savior Jesus Christ all the glory. After service, my best friend Charlotte agreed that we'd meet for lunch and talk.

Her husband Linton took the kids to their house to give us girl talk time.

Charlotte smacked her lips. "Girl. . .you can't be serious. You caught Artis smoking crack?

"Yes. Right there in our kitchen." I stirred Splenda into my coffee. "I can't afford to leave him."

"Don't start talking about walking out yet. I know it's going to be hard, but you gotta trust God for an answer. Maybe he just started using drugs."

That's one of the qualities I admired about my friend of sixteen years—her ability to analyze a negative situation and turn it into a positive. I met Charlotte in high school and we'd remained best friends since then. After we graduated from high school, I married Darius' father; Charlotte went off to college. When she graduated she accepted a job as a loan officer, met and married Linton Glasier - Vice President of the bank she worked for, and now they have twin boys who were two years younger than Darius and Marcus.

Charlotte sipped green tea, and leaned forward. "Patrice, even if he's been using drugs for a while, we know that God can take away that desire."

"I want to believe that."

Charlotte tilted her head. "Do you doubt God's power?"

"No. . .it's not that." I sighed deeply.

"Well, if you have *any* doubt, pick up your Bible and read Luke seventeen, six. And the Lord said, if ye had faith as a grain of mustard seed, ye might say unto this sycamore tree, be thou plucked up by the root, and be thou planted in the sea; and it should obey you."

Charlotte didn't have a clue. She and Linton had a potent marriage, nice home, and financial security. I wasn't complaining.

48

My marriage served as a hallmark in a neighborhood of mostly single parent homes. No, Artis and I didn't have Charlotte's and Linton's corporate jobs or a castle in Chino Hills, but we shared something far greater—quality time. That is, until Derrick came back to California with all his glitz and bling-bling to snatch Artis into a vicious cycle of sin. I prayed for hours the night before, but woke up feeling empty. . .lost. I didn't want a divorce, just a resolution. I loved the Lord with all my heart and soul, but I needed answers right now, not later.

"Patrice!"

I flinched and shifted my eyes toward hers.

Charlotte lifted her arched brows. "Did you hear what I said about prayer?"

"Sorry. . .yes, and that's a powerful verse. I pray all the time."

Charlotte pulled off her wide-brimmed lavender hat and ran her manicured nails through her layered cut. "You gotta have a long talk with Artis. Don't let me have to come to your house, 'cause you know I will."

"Girl. . .we'll be okay if he stops using drugs.

"And if he doesn't?"

I shook my head. "It can't happen again."

I truly wanted to believe that my old husband would stroll in the house and we would pickup our lives and move on. I prayed, meditated, rebuked the devil, cried, and prayed even more. Nothing changed--things got worse. Artis did not slow down. His late night escapades with his cousin increased to three times a week, sometimes four. In bed at four or five in the morning and up by six-thirty wasn't a ritual that many could withstand for long.

I hiked up the steps with groceries and called Darius to the porch. The phone rang before I could get inside the door.

"Patrice, is Artis at home?"

"No, Byron, he left for work this morning. He's not there?"

"He left for lunch at one. Haven't seen him since."

I tried to focus on my conversation with Artis' boss, but it was tough. Artis was a hard worker who'd quickly gained respect and admiration from his management team. Even if he was using drugs, his behavior made no sense and had become reckless.

"If this continues, I'll have to let him go."

"I understand. I'll tell him to call you."

I fixed dinner; Darius and I ate and talked about our day as we'd done most of the time for several months. After the dishes were washed, I sprawled out on the bed and opened the mail that had mounted on the kitchen counter for the past week. After I opened the bank envelope, I gasped and covered my mouth.

"*Overdrawn by seven-hundred forty-seven dollars and thirty-eight cents? How?*" I rumbled through the drawers for a calculator, pen and paper, and got busy. "The bank really screwed up on this one." After I'd gone through my check register, I discovered what happened… Artis.

"*Get off my back!* Some of that money is mine you know." Artis threw his jacket over the love seat, and paced from room-to-room. I followed.

"You have to tell me when you write checks. We can't pay bills if you spend all the money."

"I needed some cash and I withdrew it. I'll put it back, okay?"

"Well, what about the bills? You drained the account. Thank God the check for the rent cleared."

Artis bit his lower lip and blew out a sigh. "Baby, listen. I have some money coming from Derrick this week. He owes me four-hundred dollars, and I promise I'll put that in the bank."

My hands jetted to my hips. "You loaned Derrick *four-hundred dollars*? For what?"

"He asked me for some cash, I gave it to him. He'll pay me back. And don't cook tomorrow 'cause we're going out for dinner."

During the next several months, the television came up missing. Artis claimed that he found the front door open when he got home early one day. Several pairs of gold earrings and a necklace that he'd bought me for presents over the years—gone. He couldn't explain why they weren't in my jewelry box.

I removed my name from our joint accounts and opened separate ones. From now on, he'd never get his hands on my money or any money he'd given me. He'd already taken every valuable object from the house and either pawned or sold them. I had to find a secure place for my purse if there was one, if not I'd keep it in my bed under my pillow like I'd been doing.

Then I found an eviction notice on our door. That was it! No more praying over this matter, no more meditating, no more asking the Lord to take this away. He hadn't answered my prayers, and I couldn't figure out why. I continued going to church and reading my Bible, but my feelings had grown numb.

I called my friend Charlotte from work one day. Surprised that she picked up, I inhaled and exhaled.

"Hey, girl. . .just called to chat for a second. You busy?"

"Now you know I'm always busy. I can talk for a bit, though." She cradled the phone between her ear and shoulder while jotting down notes. "What's going on?"

"I haven't been feeling right lately. I know it's probably stress, but my appetite is gone and I can't sleep."

"Patrice. . . let me ask you something. Do you believe that God is able to do all things?"

51

Silence fell between us faster than a detonated torpedo. I wasn't ready for girlfriend's probing or sermons right now. I hadn't told her everything that had been going on in my home. Too ashamed to tell her the whole story. Besides, I called her for support and comfort, not to discuss my faith.

"You still there," she asked?

I leaned back and closed my eyes. "I go to church almost every Sunday."

"That's not what I asked you."

Charlotte wanted straight to the point facts—no shortcuts or walking in circles. That was her way, and getting around it wouldn't be easy. For once, why couldn't she understand how important it was to listen, inspire my spirit with encouraging words, maybe mention what she'd do if she were me? I didn't want to hear her rattle off Bible verses or speeches. I needed answers. Answers the Lord hadn't revealed.

"I'm doing the same things I always do."

"Okay . . .then if you're praying and trusting God, why can't you eat or sleep? When's the last time you had a physical? Are you eating. . ."

My friend's words merged and her voice faded away as if she'd hidden inside a tunnel. I pulled the receiver away and dug inside my ear canal. When I listened again, I could barely hear her voice."

"Patrice! Patrice!"

"Girl, something's wrong with this phone. Let me call you back later."

I hung up and called Darius. He sounded fine. My eyes roamed the cubicle as I took note of the stack of assignments overflowing my in-box, pictures of Darius and Marcus at the beach, and my favorite—a wooden framed photo of me and Artis on our fifth wedding anniversary. I lifted the receiver from its base and checked it, then kneeled down to check the outlets under my desk. All of the extension cords were plugged in and the phone lines properly connected. I couldn't determine the problem— maybe my mind was playing tricks on me.

Early morning crept in, darkness surrounded the room. My alarm clock vibrated across the nightstand and I rolled over to an empty bed. Twice in the past three weeks that Artis hadn't made it home nor called to say he was okay. I banged the snooze and closed my eyes for another ten minutes. I wanted to call in again, but I just took off three weeks ago. I got up and went to Darius' room, but he wasn't there.

"Hey, Mom." Darius exited the bathroom and picked up his backpack.

"Why you up so early?" I rubbed my eyes.

"Gotta get to school to have breakfast with my friends."

I folded my arms across my chest and smiled. This kid had grown into a handsome young man, looking all intellectual in his pullover grey and white sweater.

Darius kissed my cheek. "See you later, Mom."

"Have a nice breakfast with Keisha."

His face blushed behind a toothy grin. "Mom!"

"See you later, honey."

I showered, dressed, and forced down a banana and orange juice. Sleepless nights and aversion to food had added to my existing miseries. I'd cook good meals but couldn't eat, and in time my clothes sagged off my body like wet potato sacks. By 7:15 I started getting worried. I glanced at my watch and peered through the blinds. When I heard a car pull in front of the apartment and blow, I grabbed my purse and bolted out of the door. It wasn't Artis.

The long bus ride to work made me tense. I clocked in at 8:47 and ran to my desk. My supervisor sent me to the mail room for packages, and when I returned, three tapes for transcription were sitting on my desk. I scurried down the hall to the bathroom, locked myself inside a stall, and bawled for ten minutes—for what I don't know. What's wrong with me? I know my marriage and home is in chaos, but I've never felt so down in all of my life. If God won't help me, who will? I turned on the faucet, drenched my face with cold water, and rinsed my mouth to wash away the nausea that dwelled in my stomach. It was still there, but I had to return to work. I dabbed wet paper towels against my eyes to erase a sullen face. Before the day ended I'd made three more trips to the bathroom.

I waited an hour for Artis to pick me up from work. I didn't want to call his job in case he hadn't shown up, and he didn't answer any of his pages. Another bus ride back home stretched for an eternity. By the time I reached the front door, I could smell sautéed onions and garlic simmering in whatever was on the stove.

"Hey, baby. I'm fixing dinner." He extended withered arms that resembled shapeless pencils. I walked past and sat at the kitchen table.

He threw his hands up. "What's wrong with you?"

"I got off two hours ago, and I was late for work this morning. Why'd I have to catch the bus today?"

"Patrice, I'm sorry. I was out in North Hollywood helping Derrick. It won't happen again."

"That's what you said two weeks ago, and a couple of times before that. I shouldn't have to catch the bus when I pay the car note."

"I said it won't happen again." He lifted the top of the skillet, flipped the pork chops and tasted a spoonful of gravy.

"Mmm. Smells good, huh? I thought I'd cook 'cause you need to gain weight." My gaze followed Artis from pot-to-pot. He tasted food, hummed, and seemed care free as a jay bird. He whistled through sunken cheeks that looked like hollow caves. This man bore no similarity to the Artis I'd known for years. My eyes welled with tears for him and for me.

"Artis, we have to move."

He shook his head. "No, we don't. I'm doing extra work for Derrick. I'll have the money in a few weeks."

I shook my head. "In a few weeks we'll be in the streets." My hand covered my forehead. How can I make this clear? "*Darius and I* are moving."

"Nope. . .that's not happening. I'll have the money."

He stirred the rice and flipped the pork chops again, never once looking in my direction. He was oblivious to his surroundings, in denial about everything, but I had to make him understand.

I slapped my leg. "Put the spoon down and listen!"

"What do want from me? I'm trying, okay. I told you I'll have the money!"

"Yeah, and you'll spend it to get high. I'm leaving you."

He hurled a large spoon at the wall; I ducked as it flew past my head.

"Don't come at me like that!" He said, through gritted teeth.

Gravy swung from the curtains forming a small puddle on the floor. I braced myself for what might come next, but he didn't say a word. He mumbled profanity under his breath, grabbed his car keys, and left. Maybe he didn't believe me or thought I was bluffing. I'd talked about leaving so many times in the past until I couldn't believe it myself.

During the weeks that followed, insomnia took its toll and I'd become more depressed. No sleep at night equaled difficult days ahead. I huddled in a stall and cried for ten-minute periods throughout the day. My appetite was worse and I hadn't eaten a full meal in days. My plans to leave Artis played through my head like a broken record. I still loved him. Why Lord? Why did my marriage have to end like this? If I could just have my husband back. I thought I was losing my mind.

I hadn't slept at all in four days and my body craved rest, but my eyes wouldn't stay closed. I feared that if I fell asleep, I wouldn't wake up. I lay in bed late one night with the television blaring. A minister's words forced me to prop myself up on my elbows and cup my chin with a palm.

"My brothers and sisters, if you are faced with problems you can't solve, take it to Jesus. Many of you have given up; you feel your situation is hopeless and that God won't come through. Well, let me tell you something. God never fails! He just steps back at times to test your faith in Him and His word. In Hebrews eleven, verse one, the Bible says faith is the substance of things hoped for, the evidence of things not seen. Call our prayer line and let us pray with you tonight."

I picked up the phone on the nightstand, but couldn't dial. I couldn't talk to strangers about my problems even if they were saved. I hopped out of bed and squatted before the television.

"Call us; we'll keep our prayer lines open for another two hours. Tell Jesus that you love Him and you believe that He is able. If you don't want to call us, open your heart to the Lord tonight and let Him know you believe in Him and His word. All you have to do is say *yes*. Try Him—tell Him, *yes*. Hallelujah!"

As he continued to minister to the audience, a feeling of comfort washed over me. It all made sense now.

56

"*Yes,* Lord!" I clapped my hands and lifted them in praise. "*Yes,* Lord! I paced back and forth, shouting for joy. "*Yes* to Your will, *yes* to Your way! Lord I ask that You give me the strength to understand that I need You and Your guidance. I accept whatever it is that You want me to do, Lord. I will live my life to serve You. Lord, my soul says *yes!*"

I prayed for over two hours, and when I was finished, something strange happened. Thirst brought a dry, sticky feeling inside my mouth like I'd been in the desert for weeks without water. When I opened the refrigerator door, I pulled out a liter of cold water— guzzled most of it down. As I drank, I could feel something spread throughout my body—from my throat to my chest, stomach, hands, and feet. By the time I'd finished, I felt rejuvenated, and for the first night in months, I slept all night. I woke up with a renewed mind, body, and spirit. I finally had peace.

A Month Later

Lines creased between my brows as I huffed up the stairs to my new apartment with the last box. Two days of moving a little at a time had finally come to a close. I glanced over my shoulder at Charlotte who also carried a box.

"Whew! I'm glad this is over," Charlotte said. She put her hands on her hips and surveyed the boxes stacked against the wall.

We laughed. I was so thankful for Charlotte's and Linton's friendship and support. They helped me find an apartment and paid for everything. They also bought new living room furniture and home decorations that added warmth and spice to the place. I praised God every day for His grace and for friends who cared about me and my son.

"Has Artis called you?"

"Not yet, but that's good. His sister said that he's still in rehab, and he's not supposed to contact family for thirty days."

"Patrice, you know that he'll call you one day. Are you prepared for that?

I sighed and glanced upward. "Yes, Lord! And when he calls, I'll be ready."

I thought that I'd be ready. When Artis called me three weeks later, my palms got sweaty. I didn't think his call would come that soon. I still needed time to heal from open wounds, adjust to single motherhood, and to focus on my steadfast commitment to the Lord.

"Patrice, did you hear me?"

"Yes."

"Said I love you. You didn't say anything."

Chewing my bottom lip, I managed to spew out words my mind tried to resist. "Love you."

"If you love me, tell me I can come home after I leave here."

"Work on your sobriety right now. Anything else will sidetrack you from your goal. This is not the time to talk about *us*."

"But we need to talk about *us*. You don't know how hard it is to stay in this place. The food is bad, people treat us like animals. Please tell me I can come back home after this is over... really need to hear that."

I dug my nails into my arm. How can I tell him that I've moved on and my life is better without him? Lord, I need You to help me stay strong.

"Patrice, answer me!"

"Artis, let me go. I'll pray for you, but you need to pray for yourself too. Ask the Lord to heal you."

"But—"

"Call me in a few weeks. Goodnight." I hung up the phone.

Three months later

For the first time in weeks my day was free. It was Saturday so, I dropped Darius off at his friend's house to spend the night, cleaned the apartment, now I could do a few hours of reading for my sociology class. Returning to college had its challenges, but Charlotte's encouragement and tons of prayer boosted my self-confidence and I was on a mission to move forward.

Hard knocks on my door interrupted my reverie. I tried to ignore them, thinking that it could only be a solicitor since I rarely had visitors. When the knocks wouldn't stop, I pushed one eye against the peephole and saw Artis' sister standing there with her arms folded, looking disgusted. What did she want? She hadn't spoken to me since the separation. I hesitated. She banged harder.

"It's about time. Thought you'd never open the door." She yanked her purse over her shoulder and walked in.

"What's up?" I asked.

Caren folded her arms, stood in the middle of the floor, and glanced around the apartment. She ran her hand across the arm of my new rust-colored sofa and loveseat, and then plopped down.

"Artis said to tell you he's comin' home next week." She stroked her long braids.

Her eyes roamed to the Shona stone sculpture on my coffee table, the plants, and then the Synthia Saint James paintings. I wouldn't give her the satisfaction of knowing where they'd come from.

I raised my brows. "Artis hasn't talked to me about that."

"Why should he? He's your husband. And I don't like that you only been to visit him two times." She held up two fingers.

"Caren, Artis and I separated before he went to rehab. He didn't tell you?"

"Yeah, but so what! He's off drugs now and he's gotta have a place to stay. "

I crossed my legs. "I'm not going to argue with you. Tell him that I suggest he call me before he leaves rehab."

Caren tilted her head. "What's that supposed to mean?"

"He *can't* come here, and he should call me."

She smacked her lips and snatched her purse off the end table. "I don't know why he had me wastin' my time. Her hands flew to her hips. He *needs* a place to live, okay?"

"Maybe he can stay with you and Jeff until he gets on his feet."

She snapped her head back, cut me an icy stare and slammed the door behind her.

Two days later, a loud banging noise at the door could've aroused the dead. I jumped up and ran to the door. Who would be knocking at my door at 2:00 in the morning?

Darius rushed down the hallway. "Mom who's that?

"I don't know. Must be crazy—knocking at folk's door this time of night." I looked through the peephole, then covered my mouth.

"Patrice, open the door!" Artis yelled.

I didn't answer.

"Patrice, I know you're in there. Open this door!"

I cracked the door to a strong odor of alcohol mixed with whatever else he'd used. A thick screen stood as a wall of separation between us.

"Artis, why are you here?"

"You knew I was comin' home. Caren told you." He rapped against the screen door. "Open the door."

I stood there in disbelief that he'd gone back to his old habit, and now he wanted to come to my house and crash. No way. He rapped on the screen door harder, shaking it, causing a ruckus that I was sure my neighbors would soon complain about.

"Patrice, open this door!"

"No! Go away and leave us alone," Darius said, pushing between me and the screen door.

"Boy, don't talk to me like that. This is between me and your momma."

"He's right. You need to leave now."

"I'm not going anywhere! We need to talk."

I closed the door and turned toward my son.

"Mom, don't let him come back here. Please!"

Fear laced with tears smudged his caramel-colored face. His wide brown eyes drove a stake through my chest, and shame that no mother should have to see. Artis' behavior had emotionally harmed me and my son, and it was time for a change.

"Lord, please help us," I said.

I wrapped my arms around Darius and kissed his forehead. "We're okay, baby. You don't have to worry anymore."

Artis stood outside shouting, banging, screaming profanities with no regard for the neighbors who peered through windows and doors. At one point, I thought he'd burst the door down and go on a rampage. The neighbors called the police, but by the time they arrived, Artis had disappeared in the wind. Before I could file for a restraining order, he was arrested and jailed on drug possession charges. His four-month jail sentence gave me time to sort through issues and focus on the most important things in my life—God, my son, and me.

I continued working, going to school, and serving my Lord and Savior, Jesus Christ. Although our marriage was over, I didn't turn my back on Artis, but sent him a Bible and letters. I encouraged his strength through Christ with the assurance that if he accepted Him into his life, he could overcome his addiction. I ended every letter with this verse - "Therefore if any man be in Christ, he is a new creature: old things are passed away; behold, all things are become new." 2 Corinthians 5:17.

He is still struggling; I am still praying that one day he will give his life to the Lord.

Patrica A. Bridewell is a native of Los Angeles, California. Her first Christian Fiction novel, Reflections of a Quiet Storm, was released in March, 2009. She is a contributing writer to the anthology, Gumbo for the Soul – Women of Honor: Pink Edition. Her articles have been published in the Los Angeles Sentinel Newspaper, Advance for Nurses Magazine, and in several online magazines. To contact Patricia Bridewell, go to: www.patriciabridewell.com, or email her at: bridern@verizon.net

Rarefied Air
Robyn F. Johnson

My father was like a component of oxygen to me. One part oxygen and one part Nathaniel was its elemental makeup. I love my mother with all of my heart, but I breathed my father in. There's just something about the father-daughter connection. Perhaps it provides a glimpse of the divine relationship Father God desires to have with each of us and represents an innate desire to connect with something greater than ourselves.

That's how I saw my father; he was greater than I. He was eight feet tall in my eyes, with a smile that could melt your heart and a voice that could halt its beating. There was power in his voice. I wasn't a problem child, but whenever I was in trouble and he called my name, it went all through me like lightning and I didn't want to be on the receiving end of his leather belt. My mother, on the other hand, is gentle and quiet, but strong. Her voice is like flowing water. She could put out his fires and diffuse his bombs blindfolded; she'd done it for so long. He'd just laugh. Laughter was his confession – his way of admitting he was wrong.

They met as school kids and stayed together through each phase of their lives. As teenagers they vowed to love each other until death parted them. Nathaniel and Lillie had two sons, as different as night and day. Much later, when they thought they were done having children, a big-cheeked, flat-nosed, brown-eyed, bright-faced gal was born, who found her beauty in her father's eyes. They named me Robyn.

My father looked past acne scars, braces, and occasional bouts with chubbiness and called me beautiful. He saw through backtalk, stubbornness, and selfish tendencies and still called me beautiful. I desperately searched the mirror to see what he saw, but for a long time I could only see it reflected in his eyes and not through my own. He'd sense the bondage I was in and encouraged me to reach for the freedom of knowing I was fearfully and wonderfully made; I was God's handiwork. I'd forget the magnitude of my origination often, so I always appreciated the reminder. It was especially hard to remember when, as a child, I was made fun of for having a big head. We all have something that becomes fodder for the insecure – those who lash out with gusto against *your* something in hopes that no one will notice *theirs*. I knew I had a big head, but my father had passed that head down to me. So, if they laughed at me, they were laughing at my father – my oxygen.

Besides the bullies, fights, misunderstandings and heartbreaks that peppered my life's landscape, growing up wasn't too hard because at the end of every day I'd see my father. If I needed to cry, I'd wait until I got home.

"Never let 'em see you sweat," he'd say.

My mother Lillie would wrap her loving arms around me and give me hugs and kisses to dress my wounds, but it was my father who would help me to square my shoulders, grab my sword and put my armor back on so I could fight another day. He'd rattle off Biblical scriptures that I never remembered, but my heart kept every word secure. He'd tell me to hold my big head up and keep moving. He called it like he saw it, even if it meant a few hurt feelings. That was my father, short on tact, but teeming with love and purpose.

"It's hard to hit a moving target," he'd say. My mother agreed.

I can still see him standing in front of the stove when I came home from school. Glorious aromas rose from battered pots and

64

cast-iron skillets. He had no affinity for the latest and greatest in cookware back then. He was loyal to what worked and saw no need to discard things just because they were old. Something was always golden and bubbling or fiery red and sputtering. When other kids were eating fish sticks and chicken nuggets, short ribs of beef, deep dish lasagna and Seafood Newberg often greeted me after a long day. Even the air tasted good. He'd ask me how my day had been while he reached for a plate and even though I'd turned every bad thing that happened on the long walk home over and over in my mind, when I got home and saw my parents, those things didn't matter as much. The fact that they were there when I got home wasn't lost on me. I have always been an old soul. I knew, as a child, there was something very special about having the opportunity to be around my parents every day of my life. I couldn't imagine a world without them, but somewhere deep inside of me I knew the day would come.

When I look at photographs, there is always one that makes me pause. In a pure, white robe with black trim, my father stood behind a pulpit with one arm outstretched and his index finger pointing towards Heaven. His gaze following suit, he looked up with assurance. He was going to the place he pointed to. He knew that. I felt it, even from staring at the photo. His conviction and preaching were so wrapped in God's power, that at the Holy Spirit's call, I was propelled down the aisle of Shiloh Baptist Church at the age of seven. I heard the Word and responded. All I knew was Jesus loved me. My father told me so. As an elementary school student, I could not fully appreciate the transaction that took place in my heart that day, but as I reflect on the moment as a woman, I marvel at the marriage of complexity and simplicity in my action. I sought the Lord with childlike faith, but my profession had eternal implications. I earnestly asked Jesus into my heart that day and it felt like Christmas, Saturday morning cartoons and catching the ice cream truck with correct change all at once inside of me. One day, I would go to be with Jesus, just like my father, mother and brothers. I just didn't expect my father to go so soon.

If my father told me he was going to do something, I believed it. I had too much experience with him keeping his word to expect anything else. So, when he told me he would be there to give me away at my wedding, I accepted it as fact. That we are vapors and subject to be gone at any time meant nothing to me. I felt assured my father would be here until he walked me down the aisle, so I wasn't worried about it not happening. Sometimes I would sit and daydream about it. I thought about the beauty of the scenes – how one day he'd been there with open arms at the altar to welcome me into the Kingdom and how one day he'd be there to release me into the arms of the man made just for me.

Not so.

On a quiet spring morning in May, my father died. I heard him take his last breaths. It wasn't a shock to me that he passed away just a few feet from where my brother and I were sitting. Just the night before, I'd whispered in his ear, "Go home, Daddy. I'll be all right." Then I prayed a prayer I never thought I could pray. There wasn't a long introduction or scripture references involved. No vain repetitions escaped my lips on that night. It was simple and short. I bowed my head, looked toward Heaven in my heart and said, "Lord, take my father."

My father had been in relative good health, despite being overweight. His pressure, cholesterol and blood sugar were normal. He just ate the wrong things at the wrong times. He never had a weight problem until he was called to be a pastor. That's when I began to see him get heavier with each year. The weight of caring for the people settled in around his waistline. He looked just like his father, a big red man who looked like he meant business. Everything he did was loud, from walking to talking. Even his whispers could be heard several feet away. He wore tailor-made suits, wide-brim caps and aviator sunglasses that covered his light eyes. I never could classify them as one color because they would change a lot. He was tall, round on top and skinny on the bottom. I used to call him my "Blow Pop."

"I got your Blow Pop," he'd say, squinting at me. Then he'd smack his stomach with both hands and shake it around. "It took me years to grow this." It took years and lots of trips to the grocery store. My father loved going to markets. He'd always come back with all kinds of treasures to show me. One trip to the grocery store changed his life. He fell hard on his way out. Our evening walks were different after that. He was struggling to keep up with me as we walked around the mall, but his pride was pushing him and I could tell. I thought he needed to see a doctor. He wasn't healing. It wasn't normal. When he finally went to the doctor, the testing began. Everyone poked and prodded trying to figure out what was wrong. In January of 2005, we all knew the answer. It was the "C." Not just any C, but a rare form: multiple myeloma.

"You *would* get a rare cancer," I teased. He smiled at me, faintly.

I wasn't too concerned about it. He'd told me he'd be at my wedding to give me away and since I didn't even have a boyfriend I knew his last days were far off. I figured he would beat it and have a testimony and that was that. What else could I have thought about a six-foot, 280-pound, take no prisoners, make it happen and keep it moving type of a man? I had never known my father to back away from a fight, real or imagined. He took everything head

67

on. He did everything full throttle. It was his nature to be that way. That's why I didn't understand what he meant at first about wanting to go home. At that point, he'd been confined to his bed for about two months. He couldn't walk anymore; his muscles had atrophied. He laid there in bed looking at me like a little kid who had been stealing cookies and got caught. He was embarrassed. He was sorry. He said it again.

"I wan' go 'ome," he slurred.

"You *are* home, Daddy," I said. He looked and me and shook his head sharply.

"No," he said.

He pointed to the sky and I gasped. I put my hand over my mouth and shook my own head back and forth. I got it. He wanted to go *home*. The place he had pointed to in the early days of his ministry. Then, it had been captured in a black and white photograph, but now he was closer than he'd ever been in living color and there was a peace in his eyes like I'd never seen. I cursed that peace. I wanted him to stay. I stood there on my twenty-eighth birthday, with balloons in my hand from work and my purse still on my shoulder looking at my father in disbelief. It was the first day of school for me. Faith showed up as the teacher. There would be no substitutes and there was sure to be homework, but was I ready for the test?

I was confused. I couldn't accept that my father wouldn't be healed. I didn't care what he struggled to say and I didn't understand why he was saying it. I would continue to pray and there would be a miracle. That's all there was to it. That's what faith was to me. It was an action word. If I believed in something hard enough, it would happen. I wouldn't let what I saw deter me from my belief. My father couldn't walk or sit up without help, but I believed he would be healed and he would get up out of the bed on his own. I believed it like I knew the sun would come up in the morning. It was done.

While I was praying and believing, so was my father. He'd preached the gospel, calling sinners to repentance and salvation. He'd crusaded in Africa and stood on the equator. He'd answered the call. He'd built a church. He'd sacrificed his life for the walk. He'd finished the work. He could see the finish line in the distance and he pressed towards it. He longed to see the face of the One who'd rescued him from a life of obscurity, infidelity and excess. He wanted to lie at the feet of the Savior and bask in the glory of His presence. He was laying down his armor and I was angry. The timing was wrong. I started to cry. My mother started to preach. She ran through the saints and the hurdles they faced. Job made it through and so had Daniel and Joseph. Why wouldn't Nathaniel? Nathaniel could, but he was tired. He was just a man, like Moses, David and every other person who'd answered the call. I looked at my father, the man who'd earned degrees in theology, and was overwhelmed by his humanity.

"I tay it bah," he said when he saw the tears rolling down my cheeks.

Some things can't be taken back. I'd heard my father loud and clear. He was ready to see the Master and I went on a faith mission to make sure he wouldn't make the trip so soon. Two weeks into my pleading and praying and fasting, God spoke to me very clearly in my spirit. I was driving home from my parent's house when it happened. He told me he was preparing me. I felt the words so clearly that I replied out loud, "For what?" The Lord responded in my heart and told me He was taking my father home – his real home – just as he'd requested. The Lord kept His promise, but He showed me something supernatural before He answered my father's prayer. When my father had fallen, his bones were fractured, and the cancer that had been residing in his marrow infiltrated his body. One of the spots was on his spine. As a result, in his later days, he could not sit up straight or even on his own. One night, about ten days before he died, my father had a glow on his face. Mom and I were tending to him when we saw it.

"I'm gin' owa dis room," he said.

With that, he began to sit up. He grabbed the rails on the bed and pulled himself up and sat on the edge of the bed in seconds. His spine was as straight as a ruler. He sat there for a moment, strong and glowing with his feet reaching for the floor. In a blink, the glow was gone and he looked around in confusion. He hunched over and we helped him to lie back down. My mother and I kept staring at each other. It was like the time when my then two-year old nephew Travis fell forward on the basement steps. We all saw him falling parallel to the floor and at the last minute, his direction changed and he was perfectly vertical. It was just like that. You knew God's presence was in the room. You knew He had dispatched an angel to allow finite beings a supernatural glance into His realm.

I can still see my father sitting up tall and straight on the edge of that bed. For me, it was a reminder that God can do anything. My faith in total healing for my father was akin to the faith my father had, but my father's idea of healing and mine were different. My father wanted healing that was beyond this world. The morning of his transition, I stood by his bedside listening to him breathe. A laborious gurgling sound came and went as his chest heaved. I began to understand his way of thinking, but even as I grasped the concept, the air in my lungs followed behind him the moment he left. I struggled to recover my breath and looked up at the ceiling and waved, wondering if he saw me or if he was just instantly gone. I looked down at his face. His eyes were still open, but just barely. He had been comatose for about a day, so there were no last words, no parting blessings. All that remained was a testament to the beauty of what his soul beheld. Tears were welled up in his eyes; the tears had not been there in the minutes prior. There is a depth of silence born from death. It's like sitting outside at night while snow is falling. No traffic from man or machine, but quietness so thick, it demands acute awareness. The intensity of the moment fell around me like fat, billowy flakes. I studied my father's face and was paralyzed by his hollowness. I don't remember when the men from the funeral home came, but I know I held the door when they carried my father's body out of my childhood home. I took a few steps after them and stopped at the top of the concrete stairs. My father was gone and I was still alive. I had remembered telling God if he took my father, then he might as well take me too. I didn't think I could survive without him, but it wasn't until he died that I began to put it all together – this thing called faith. I needed his absence to see what had always been there.

In the Bible, Isaiah wrote that in the year King Uzziah died, he saw the Lord in all of His glory, high and lifted up. In the year Nathaniel died, I saw faith unrolled from Heaven like a scroll. It had been something to talk or sing about, something to lift my hands about. It was now something I had to live out. God had been laying the foundation in the background and was waiting for the right time to show me the plans for the house He was planning to build within me. It took about three months after losing Dad for that moment to come. I was sitting in my apartment in the middle of the floor when my grief exploded. I started screaming.

"I don't have a father!"

I kept screaming the words over and over. Tears and saliva drenched my face as I screamed. I'd take a long breath and push out the phrase with more force each time. Just when I was about to scream it one more time, God spoke to my heart quietly in the midst of my clamor.

"*I* am your Father."

Peace descended on me like I'd never felt before or since. I could no longer scream or cry. God touched my heart and drew out the anguish. I sat there for a moment, dumbfounded. I tried to cry again and couldn't. Although I had been at the service and watched as my father's body was lowered into the earth...my heart had not even begun to stir the dust to which he had returned. God buried my father on that day as I sat in the middle of my living room floor.

Now, He could show me the blueprint.

Everything I'd seen up to that moment was preparing me to truly understand God, the father. A father is a man of his word. His hands hold you up when you are devoid of strength. He shields you from blows meant for you. He makes a way when there is no way. He never leaves or gives up on you. He always sees your beauty and loves you without condition. He works to correct what is wrong and fixes what is broken. And, when the time is right, He pushes you out of your comfort zone so you can fly. My father stood in as a substitute for all of these things until I beheld my Heavenly Father.

I could see God so clearly, but my ears were closed. He was calling me a little higher for His purpose, but it would take four years for me to truly listen. I spent those four years knowing God had kept His word in my life, but refused to act on what He was trying to teach me. I knew He had called me to write, but I ignored the call. I remember having dreams where I would hear a voice saying, "Write. Write. Write." I would wake up suddenly and look around; it felt like someone was speaking it just down the hall. I'd start to work on something and then throw up my hands and give up. I'd enter a contest, get rejected and pelt myself with handfuls of "told you so."

I'd crossed the abyss of losing my father, but refused to scale the mountain of my purpose. I'd cry out to the Lord asking Him what He wanted me to do. It always came back to writing. I'd ask Him if there was anything else I could do. No one knew me. I wasn't a *real* writer. I wasn't good enough. Who'd buy my books? Who, besides a handful of family and friends, would even care? All of my questions were selfish. I cared only about my comfort and had thought nothing of the gift He gave me. It was His gift, not mine. If people rejected me, they were really rejecting Him and since He can handle rejection, I began to wonder if I should at least give it a try.

One day, while going through the motions at work, I had a meltdown. I felt so insignificant. I felt like an ant that hadn't brought anything back to the colony in a long time. I labeled myself an outcast, an infidel and one who was wasting my days. I'd stopped caring about the way I looked. My hair was back in a ponytail. No lipstick. No smile. No joy. My stomach was so big that it pressed against the button on my jeans and left a mark above my navel. I sat in my cubicle and stared at the tan fabric walls. My legs started shaking like I was cold. I had to escape the walls. I put on my corduroy jacket, stepped out into the hall and pressed the down button on the elevator. My legs were still shaking. I walked across the parking lot, got into my car and called my brother, Rodney. In thirty minutes I poured out everything I was feeling. My legs stopped shaking. He asked me what I wanted out of life and I didn't have an answer. He told me to go home, think about it and write it down. He said I needed to begin to

73

speak positive things into my life instead of continually regurgitating negative prophecies.

I thought, "This is crazy." It couldn't be that simple. If it was, everyone would do it. As I walked back toward the building, I got bold. I got pretty charged up and wanted to see if what he said really worked. I felt like I needed a change of scenery at work, so I pointed to the building and said out loud, "In forty days, I will not be here." When I got back to my cube, I said, "Two weeks notice." For the first time in my life, I'd taken an active role in my life's direction. I didn't know how these things would come to be, but I believed with every part of me they would. Two weeks from the day I said it, I had an interview. My company had submitted my resume for an assignment months earlier and now the customer wanted to meet me and one other co-worker. We won the contract. It gave me chills. I wasn't out of the building in forty days, it was more like sixty, but I wasn't complaining. I was sitting in a new office on the other side of town. My faith got stronger. I'd spoken it and it happened. My brother wasn't crazy after all. My father's voice echoed in my ears: "It's hard to hit a moving target." I was definitely on the move.

By God's power, I began to attract positive things into my life. When bad things came along, as they are sure to in this fallen world, they didn't affect me as much because I was so determined to be positive. My endometriosis would act up, my debt seemed insurmountable and I was dealt a good dose of unrequited love, but I was undaunted. If I needed to cry, I would, but right after I was done I'd ask the Lord to fill me with joy. He did it every time. I stopped watching the news in the mornings before work and began to turn on spiritual teachings instead. The words came to me again. "Write. Write. Write."

At first, I made a lot of excuses. My job was demanding, I was tired when I got home. Blah, blah, blah. But one night when I was tired of Robyn, I got down on the floor, stretched out my hands and feet and laid face down. I cried from my soul directly into the carpet. "I surrender."

In the days that followed I learned surrender is a daily act. You don't just say it and it's done. You have to be willing, every day, to give yourself over to what God has for you. Some days I am an open vessel and some days I don't feel like being used at all. Just like Paul, I find myself doing things I hate. The good that I would do, I find myself not doing. I thank God for putting real men and women in the Bible to let us know that in this journey of faith we are sometimes up and sometimes down, but we are never consumed.

My pastor preached a sermon that truly propelled me forward. He spoke of a time in his ministry when he wondered whether he should give up or go on. He pleaded with God for a fresh word to give him direction. God gave him Isaiah 43:18-19, which reads: *"Remember not the former things, nor consider the things of old. Behold, I am doing a new thing; now it springs forth, do you not perceive it? I will make a way in the wilderness and rivers in the desert."*

I felt like I'd been given a push on a swing. I began to kick my legs stronger and stronger until I was so high, I was flying. I didn't want to fight God anymore. I didn't want to fight what He put inside of me, so I hung up my boxing gloves. I don't fight my creativity anymore. I embrace it. I live in a world now where I wake up every day wanting to write and stay up late just trying to get a few more words out. I was born to be a writer. I got it from my father.

"I'm too lazy to write a book," he'd say. "But you? You should write a book."

As I work on my first novel, my thoughts often return to watching my father write sermons in the laundry room. I'd tip in and stare at his back as he hunched over his desk combing through the Bible and scribbling down broken thoughts. These days, when I look at the sermon notes he wrote, I shake my head. They might as well be hieroglyphics to me. But when he preached, God wove it into something beautiful.

I believe God makes everything beautiful in its season. He plants a seed of faith inside each of us. I see our world as a garden and God as the Master Gardener. He sends alternating rain and light and waits for the growth to happen. He rejoices when we choose Him and open ourselves up to bloom in His will.

Each day, I put my foot out and marvel at the path He is paving before me. With each step I take, my faith multiplies. In July of 2010, I started getting down on the floor to pray every morning and ask Him to direct me and use me for His glory. I asked Him to allow me to touch lives through the gift He gave me. I asked Him to put my story in a book. He did it. His answer is the reason why you are reading these words right now. It's also why I still breathe in the absence of my father. I have a new source of oxygen and His name is Jesus. I'm flying in rarefied air. Join me. Answer the call.

Robyn F. Johnson, the self-proclaimed Christian Fictionista, seeks to spin tales to open eyes to spiritual truths and win hearts to Jesus. She is currently working on her first fiction novel and has faith that it will be published in 2011. She lives in Baltimore, Maryland with her family. Website: www.robynfjohnson.com

Through the Fire–My 9-11 Memories
Sheryl Howard Fields

> I say to God my Rock,
> "Why have you forgotten me?
> Why must I go about mourning,
> oppressed by the enemy?" ... Psalm 42:9

My day started out much as it did on any other day, with a slow, lazy awakening, prayer and the news. I left the house earlier than normal because I had to vote and I didn't want to do it after work. As I walked to the voting poll, I looked up and thought how beautiful and clear the sky was and that the clouds looked like fluffy, white, decorative pillows against the blue background.

After I voted, I came back home and decided that I wasn't going in to work. The day was just too beautiful and I wanted to get out and enjoy it. Suddenly, I remembered that I was scheduled for a training class and that the company would be charged whether I attended or not, so I reluctantly left for work.

Just as I reached the stairs to the subway, I stopped short causing the woman behind me to bump into me. I told her I was sorry, but I couldn't go to the train without making my daily request to God and she decided to wait with me while I did, asking that I include her in the request. So I asked God, as I did everyday, to send the angels to watch over us, lead, guide and protect us throughout the day and to take us safely to our destinations and bring us safely home again, if it was His holy will. By 7:30 a.m., I was on my way, a full hour earlier than usual with no idea that I would definitely need that prayer to be answered. My faith was about to be shaken and renewed in a powerful way.

After getting off at Chambers Street, I toyed with the idea of going upstairs to the post office to mail my grandchildren's birthday gifts, but decided to wait until later. I entered the building, stopped by the cafeteria for coffee and arrived at my office by 8:20 a.m. and made preparations to head up to my 9:00 a.m. class.

Still thinking of making a dash to the post office, I started toward the elevator and changed my mind. Three times I left my desk to go up to my class on either the eighty-fourth or eighty-six floor, only to change my mind after getting on the elevator and backing off before the doors fully closed. On the last attempt, I returned to my desk to get my glasses from the file cabinet drawer even though I had a pair in my purse. For some reason, I just couldn't get started, so I sat back down and logged on to read my emails and listen to my voice mail messages. The telephone display showed that it was 8:40 a.m. Five minutes later, at 8:45 a.m., there was a tremendous crash from above and the building started swaying back and forth throwing me around the office as I attempted to get my balance, my chair rolled uncontrollably around the office. Above me, I could hear ceiling tiles falling like the sound of dominoes. With the building still moving, I grabbed my purse and turned toward the stairs just as a large three drawer file cabinet slid towards me. I was pulled from the office by a co-worker as he ushered other employees towards the stairs. Praying for God to help us, he instructed us to leave the building as quickly as possible.

The stairs became immediately crowded as people rushed to get out. We had to stop several times due to crowding and injured people being brought down by co-workers.

The air was filled with dust and my breathing was becoming irregular. It was hot and stuffy in the stairwell. As we went down, firemen began to pass us on the way upstairs, carrying heavy equipment and urging us to stay calm, stay to the right of the stairs to allow them to come up and to just keep moving. They kept reassuring us that everything was okay and that it was safe, but to leave as quickly as possible in an orderly fashion. One woman wanted to go back and get her purse, but I held on to her hand and kept walking. I told her she could come back and get it later after things cleared up; she agreed and continued on with the rest of us.

The heat was becoming more unbearable and I felt like I couldn't make another step. The pain in my right leg was excruciating and I had to keep repeating every prayer I'd ever learned and every Psalm and Bible verse I could remember to keep myself moving. Sweat was pouring off of everyone and we were all beginning to dehydrate and become thirsty. The firemen broke open vending machines with their axes and gave us water and juice to drink and take down with us.

I had been counting the floors and made myself stop because it seemed that we were taking forever to get out. We finally reached the twenty-third floor. Something suddenly happened to cause the hall to fill with smoke and dust and we were directed to go back up to the twenty-fifth floor to find another stairwell. Later, I found out that Tower Two had been hit and the smoke and debris was from the other building and the windows that had exploded from the impact of the attack.

After making several stops, we arrived at the fifth floor, only to be stopped again. Water was flowing down the stairwell like a waterfall. We were again told to go back up. People began to panic and some started crying. One woman kept repeating "we're going to die" over and over again. I told her I was not going to die because angels were protecting me, and if she wanted to live, she'd better hold on to me because I was getting out of that building and going home. Nobody wanted to go back, so we were just standing there watching people cry and trying to stay strong for those that were starting to lose it. Then, with everything that was happening, the lights went out. We couldn't see anyone or anything around us. Someone yelled out "the Captain says come back up." We still didn't move. I sent a prayer to God that we needed an angel to guide us and we needed him right now. After about two minutes, a fireman appeared right in front of us with two flashlights and told us not to go back up, but to follow him and he led us down to the Plaza level. I looked around to thank him, but he wasn't there and I vaguely remember wondering where he had gone, but thanked God for his angelic presence and help in getting us downstairs.

We were moving again, being led around the perimeter of the wall, trying to avoid falling objects. There was debris everywhere. I couldn't tell where we were. A fireman yelled at us to get out, to move fast and not to look out onto the plaza. I and many of the others probably would never have looked if the firemen hadn't said anything, but as soon as he did, everyone focused their eyes in that direction. I wish I never had. I couldn't believe what I was seeing. Total disaster; glass, plants, broken parts of the building and things I don't want to remember were scattered all over the plaza

I was so tired. I felt like I couldn't take another step, and at that point, I just wanted to sit down and give up. The woman in front of me collapsed to the floor and her co-workers were urging her to get up and move. I wanted to cry, but couldn't. The over-large planters and trees were scattered everywhere and we had to climb over them, but I could barely lift my legs. I fell to my knees and two co-workers helped me over the larger pieces and encouraged me to go on. The pain in my knees was horrible, but they kept telling me that I could do it until we came out of the building. Once we were outside everyone took off at a fast pace, so I lost track of the people I was with.

The street looked like the movie set of a war zone. Cars, trucks and everything in sight was destroyed and covered in dust. It was as if the world had turned black and white. There was no color. The dust had taken the color out of the world. The sight and the thought of what had to have taken place to make this happen, took my breath away.

I still had no idea what had happened, but the sight caused me to start hyperventilating. A young couple took me to an emergency vehicle for oxygen, but there wasn't any. The fireman told me to sit on the side of the truck and take deep breaths to calm down. The couple patiently waited with me.

I sat there for a few minutes, but I got a strange feeling and I heard a voice telling me to get up and keep moving, but I didn't move. I heard it again, this time loud and clear, shouting at me to get up and move now! I got up, told the couple that we needed to go. We started walking with a group of people down Church Street. As we neared Chambers Street, the firemen started yelling for us to run. I heard a noise and turned just in time to see Tower Two come down. The young man I was with pushed his girlfriend and me down to some subway stairs and laid on top of us to try to protect us from the cloud of dust that was flying down the street and around the corner bringing with it bits of broken glass and other objects.

The dust and debris was so thick that everything seemed to disappear. It was as if time stood still and all sound stopped; black and white, moving in slow motion. I'm not sure how long it stayed that way. People started moving at a faster speed, then they were running, mouths opened as if screaming and I still heard no sounds coming from them. I began to walk fast with the crowd. I had no sense of direction, not sure where I was going, just moving, lost and alone. I had become separated from the young couple.

Sound came rushing back abruptly and I heard someone scream, "Oh, my God!" I looked back to where she was staring and saw Tower One, my home away from home for the past eight years, the place where my friends and work family had shared each others' joys and sorrows, come tumbling down in one big swoosh as if it was taking its last breath. No other sounds could be heard; just deadly quiet, then the noise began again.

Uncontrollable thoughts started flowing from my mind like a windstorm. Why was this happening? Who was attacking us? Why? Why? Innocent babies were kept in the nursery during business hours. Where were those sweet little angels with their cute baby smiles and chatter? Did someone get them all out in time? Where are my friends? I'm all alone and so tired, but I have to keep moving. What's going to happen next? Are there more of them coming? Keep moving. I wanted to cry, but I had no tears. I was all alone and I had no one to hold on to. Everyone else seemed to be with someone, but I was all alone. Why? I wanted to feel something, anything, but I was just too tired and too numb. Where am I? I have to call someone! Oh, God, please don't let my mother or my family see this. I have to call someone! That clock can't be right! It can't be ten o'clock. It has to be later than that. Is it really just ten o'clock? Oh Lord, please help me. Where is everyone that I know? I can't think anymore. Keep moving. I couldn't stop the thoughts that were running rampant in my mind as I wandered aimlessly from the Towers and the disaster.

Someone shook me, bringing my mind back in focus. Several co-workers from New Jersey saw that I was alone and disoriented and wanted me to come with them, but I needed to go in the opposite direction. I needed to go downtown to get home to Brooklyn. I thanked God for seeing familiar faces, but I had to trudge on, still alone.

None of the phones, cell or landlines were working and I still needed to call someone. As I neared the end of Chinatown, I found one phone working with a long line of people waiting to make calls. Someone let me take their place and I called home to say that I was on my way home walking towards the Manhattan Bridge. I asked my husband to please call me mother and let her know that I was okay.

I walked on, tired, weary and dirty. Moving along with the masses, I headed toward the bridge. If I could just get enough energy to make it across that bridge, then I knew I could make it home even if I had to crawl.

Just as I got to the bridge, a van turned in front of me and I knocked on the window. I asked the man inside to please give me a ride across the bridge. He looked at me as if I were from another planet, so I asked him again. He told me to get in. I didn't know him. I didn't ask his name, we didn't talk... just rode along in silence next to the throng of people trying to get to the other side of the river into Brooklyn. He made one stop and let a woman on crutches get in. I helped her in and we continued to ride in silence. He will never know how much that ride meant to me, but his act of kindness is imprinted in my heart and mind forever.

At the foot of the bridge, I rejoined the walking masses headed toward Fulton Street, asking God to give me the strength to make one more step and then another and another.

People were giving out water and chairs were being set out for people to take a few minutes rest. Businesses were offering the use of their bathroom facilities and wet towels to wipe the grime from our faces. Religions, races, creeds and colors had disappeared. A miracle had occurred in the midst of this crisis. We had all become one, one people sharing one horrific, heartrending crisis. We had all become one family, one nation under God, indivisible, united in an effort to comfort and ease the grief and pain we were all sharing.

After a brief rest, I started out again still giving myself pep talks to just keep moving, asking God for more strength to make it home, to take one more step. Two more blocks, "You can do it." One more block. Finally, St. James Place, just a few more steps. As I turned the corner, my upstairs neighbor Marie was there waiting. She hugged me and told me how glad she was that God had allowed me to make it home.

Inside the hallway at last, just a few more steps and I would be home. More hugs and tears from another next door neighbor.

Just a few more steps to my apartment, just one click of the key and I'd be home at last. No hugs here. Nothing and I'm too numb to care. I needed to call my Mom and my family to reassure them that I was okay. At their urging, I went to the nearest hospital to ensure that I was okay.

After several hours, I was released only to find that I was alone again. I had been left alone at the hospital with no way to get home, so I walked home.

I was completely drained, tired, dirty and hurting both mentally and physically. I silently cried out to God, "Help me, please! I want to lie down and sleep so that when I wake up this nightmare will be over. Please God, help me to wake up and make this go away! Make it all go away! Just start the day over again and make it go away!

My blood pressure was way too high. My skin hurt. It was stinging and burning. My eyes were burning and hurting. I hurt all over. I needed to take a bath and scrub away the dust and dirt that was caked on my body. I wanted to get rid of the clothes I was wearing. I wanted to wash away the smell of death from my nostrils. I wanted to feel safe again, but I didn't think I could. I was scared, but I couldn't afford to break down. I couldn't because I was alone and plagued by all that I had seen.

Too tired to deal with anything anymore, I dozed off and on in the recliner and finally fell into a deep sleep from sheer exhaustion.

I awakened and realized that I was truly blessed and grateful to God for sparing me and my friends. I know now that I am not alone. I am not unloved because God is always with me, holding me in His arms, sending His angels to protect me. I was left here for a reason and I have a new outlook on life and I plan to live it to the fullest extent.

I awoke at 2:00 a.m., September 12, 2001 and new day. I survived hell. I felt its heat and endured the pain. I saw its destructive power. I've been through the fire, so I know my life is not in vain.

Sheryl Howard Fields is a native of Savannah, GA and currently resides in Brooklyn, NY. Devoted to family and friends she knows that faith can definitely move mountains, if you believe. She credits her joy of reading and writing to her mother the late Valerie Holland Howard who taught her that you can go anywhere in a book.

God is Listening
Michele D. Rose

$\mathcal{J}$'m a pretty girl. I'm smart. I'm funny. I'm the life of the party. Everyone seems to love me and guys are always hanging around me. But no matter what, I never feel good enough because I'm overweight. No matter how cute, funny, or popular I am, being big seems to be unaccepted by everyone – especially men. But I love myself, right? I'm okay with who I am, right? I so much want to believe that I'm worthy of better treatment. But every time I believe that, a man comes along and proves me wrong.

Nothing hurts worse than when you realize the man you're dating or in love with has issues with your appearance. Even though this guy I was dating never directly came out and said anything, I slowly began to see signs that he had issues. Stupid me! I was so excited that someone attractive was paying attention to me, that I couldn't even see that I embarrassed him. Apparently being cute wasn't enough. It's the size of the rest of me that mattered. Dear God, I hope I won't be alone for the rest of my life. All the men I've dealt with have mistreated me in some fashion. I went from a liar and a cheater to an alcoholic who took money from me, all the way down to a brother who wasn't sure who or what he wanted.

My real first love was the biggest deceiver I had ever encountered. Although I had been slightly hurt before, I had never been hurt the way he hurt me. He was new, different, and appeared to be legit. He was genuine and shared everything with me. Eventually I grew to trust him, which was something I was afraid to do. He broke that trust. Of all the men before him, I never thought he would do this to me. I shared my past hurts and pains with this man, and he somehow did the same thing to me that the others did. He used me for sex and lied to me for months. He took my kindness for weakness and took total advantage of me. What was it all for? What did he gain? Why does this keep happening to me? I must be doing something wrong. Is it my fault? I just don't get it. I'm smart and educated and I've got a pretty face. I thought that's all men needed. God, I can't keep going thru this. It hurts too badly. I just want to be happy. Is that possible? Will I ever meet someone who loves me for me and can treat me the way I deserve to be treated?

I met another man; a beautiful man with a fabulous body. Eager to find love in any form I could get it, I let him move in with me only to later find out he was an alcoholic. Not sure how I ended up in yet another jacked up relationship, I had to pray diligently to find my way out. Praying was hard, though, because I knew I wasn't living my life in a way that was pleasing to God. I was living with a man who wasn't my husband, having pre-marital sex whenever I wanted, drinking, smoking, and barely going to church on Sundays. Did I really expect God to rescue me? I wanted Him to, but knew I was not worthy of His help.

At one point, I figured that I might as well stay with him. I was older now, and was sure that it would be much harder for me to find a man. I was still overweight, so that made it worse. Just stay. So what if he drinks all day and all night, at least I've got somebody, right? I mean, having an alcoholic boyfriend is better than being alone. But I'm tired God. I know I may not be doing everything right, but I heard somewhere that you would never leave me nor forsake me. I didn't know a lot of Bible verses (especially since I barely went to church), but at that point in my life, I wanted so badly to know if God was there... if He was listening to my plea for help. I really wanted to leave, but didn't know how. I knew that God had something better for me, but I was scared. I didn't want to be alone for the rest of my life. I wanted more for myself. Please Lord, rescue me.

I experienced a lot of heart break before turning thirty years old. Man after man, failed relationship after failed relationship was my standard of living. It was beginning to be a way of life for me. Almost as if I wasn't happy unless I was being mistreated and abused, lied to and misused. When I would meet a decent guy, I would sometimes think he was dorky or too nice, so I'd bounce. After thirteen long years, I'd had enough. At first, I was tired of dating the same predictable type of man. But then, I began to get tired of being sick and tired and made up my mind to do what I could to snatch my life back.

After the very painful breakup with the alcoholic, it took me approximately one year to heal. I cried non-stop for weeks and weeks. After the crying stopped, I tried to pick myself up, but all I kept hearing in my head was, "you will be alone for the rest of your life, just call him, he will come back." But I refused to listen. Somewhere, deep down in the fiber of my being, I knew that God had a plan. Sometimes I wasn't all the way sure, but I wanted so bad to believe in my heart that He was there each time I was offended, and that He saw each and every tear. I believed that He heard every prayer, and that one day He was going to rescue me. I just didn't know when. The enemy constantly taunted me and incessantly tempted me, and eventually, I caved.

Although I didn't go back to the alcoholic, I did decide to date again. But this time, I attempted to date with a different mission in mind. My mindset was to simply find a man so I wouldn't be alone. I dated a guy here and there, but when they wanted sex, I became instantly turned off. There was maybe one or two brothers I was comfortable enough to be intimate with, but having random sex with random guys – no matter how mad and disgusted I was – I just couldn't live that way.

During this season of random dating, I met a really nice guy. Pepper was his name. He was much younger, about six years to be exact. He was a big guy, but seemed to be a gentle giant. No matter how much I wanted to discount him and make excuses for why I couldn't date him, he was very genuine and I could sense it. Although I was still somewhat "damaged goods," I wanted to see what he was about, so I let him in. We talked, went for walks, and dated for a few months. It was nice. Although I could tell he was attracted to me, he never acted on it. He never once tried to touch me inappropriately. In fact, I think we waited several weeks before our first kiss. After what I had been through, this behavior was very unusual, but I liked it.

One day out of the blue, after months of really liking each other, he confessed that he was in a relationship. *What? I knew he was too good to be true!* I thought to myself. Then I thought, *Oh no, he didn't!* Man was I angry! Although he broke it to me gently, I was still mad. I felt that he completely wasted my time. But since we had not been intimate with each other, I guess it wasn't a complete waste of time. He further confessed that although he was in a relationship, he was miserable. He wanted to get out, but didn't know how. He loved her, but she was unstable and emotionally abusive and he couldn't take it anymore. Since I had been in several unhealthy and unstable relationships myself, I gave him the best advice I could. He then chose to leave me alone and go back to her to work things out. Very angry, I almost cussed him out. But I decided to just move on. Even still, I thought about him often and wondered how he was doing. Every couple of months or so, we would call each other to see how things were going, but because he was still with her, I had to let go.

The next phase of my life was very self-defining. While I was in school trying to finish my degree, I sometimes wondered if I would ever be in a relationship with a decent man. I met and dated a couple more guys after Pepper, sad to say, they were all losers. After so much frustration, I got tired of the same dating game and tired of the enemy chasing my mind. That's when I decided to give God another shot. One day, my cousin invited me to visit a new church that I had never heard of before – The Lion of Judah. The name of the church was weird to me, but I took a chance and went anyway. The pastor, Bishop Frank L. Gibson III, absolutely blessed me that day. He was so good; I kept going back for weeks and weeks to see if he would ever have a bad day in the pulpit. But he never did. He preached life-changing sermons every single time. No matter how hard I tried to ignore what I heard, something was happening inside of me. I knew I needed to change. I wanted to change. But in my flesh, I wanted to continue living the way I was used to living. I struggled with God for several weeks, and guess who won? Within two months, at the tender age of thirty two, I made a commitment to God to become celibate and to save myself for marriage. At that time, I had not considered how hard it would be. I only knew that my way of doing things was no longer working and I needed a new plan. I began believing in my heart that God loved me and because He sent His son Jesus to die for me and my messy self, the least I could do was try to live right. So I did.

Approximately two years into my celibacy Pepper called me. We met for coffee and learned that we both really wanted to try this relationship thing again, but unfortunately, he was still emotionally attached. Remembering our talk a few years prior, he wouldn't dare start something new with me. So, instead of us trying to force something to work, I told him to call me when he got himself together. "If I'm still single, we can try one more time; but I can't promise you I'll wait," I told him. We hugged and went our separate ways. It's funny; even though he was still attached to her, I felt weird about letting him go. There was something special about him but I just couldn't put my finger on it. For years I would think about him and wonder what he was doing, how he was doing, and if he was still single.

While successfully living a life of celibacy, I was charged with the task of doing constructive and positive things to occupy my time instead of doing destructive things that would keep me feeling defeated. Still seeking my undergraduate degree, I threw myself into my studies and was carrying a full load while working full-time. I then became actively involved in ministry and began seeking God's face. Not knowing exactly what I was doing, God was slowly moving me into my destiny. I was active in the Marketing Ministry, Women's Ministry, and then the Singles Ministry. One day, my beloved pastor appointed me to serve as co-ministry leader for the Evangelism Ministry. Scared to death, I was learning to trust God. I began feeding and ministering to the homeless and to the inmates in prison. I began fasting and then led others to fast with me. With no bad relationships to hinder me and no sexual relationships to get me off track, I was on my way to the life God promised.

Of course, the enemy is always prowling around looking for someone to devour (1 Peter 5:8) and I was no exception. As I was getting stronger and stronger in my life of celibacy, everyone around me was getting engaged or married. I wanted to believe all the things God promised me, but my mind kept telling me it would never happen. As I desperately tried to hold on to my faith and the things God had showed me, it was getting harder and harder to remember His promises. I began feeling as if God had forgotten me. On one particular night, I was at a birthday celebration for one of my best girlfriends. Although a sweet, successful and outgoing sister, she was not as actively involved in the church as I was. During this birthday celebration, in front of all her family and friends, her boyfriend stood up and pulled out a ring and proposed to her. Everyone was shocked and I was speechless. She is a very close friend of mine, so I was genuinely happy for her. However, I was immediately forced to hold myself together so I wouldn't break down and cry in front of everyone. But when I realized that my tears would be misinterpreted and translated into tears of joy for my friend, I opened the flood gates and cried my heart out.

After dessert, I gave my soon-to-be-married girlfriend a big hug of congratulations and left the restaurant. As I ran to my car, I couldn't get there fast enough. I knew I had more bawling to do. I thought to myself, "God, are you serious? After all the serving, sacrificing and giving I have been doing, you send *her* a husband? I don't understand God. Am I doing something wrong? Should I give more? Should I fast more? When will it be my turn? Are you listening God? I mean, she goes to church, but a lot of believers do that. She doesn't do half of what I do for You, Lord and yet You bless her? Do you still love me God?"

Upon arriving at my house, I wiped my tears and went inside. Still feeling defeated and ignored, I began thinking about all the sex I was missing. I started thinking about how nice it would be to spend an intimate evening with someone. I wanted to feel a man, smell a man, and be next to a man. Even if just for one night, my body was suddenly yearning. Doing the opposite of what I was feeling and thinking, I told the devil that he was a liar and that God had not forsaken me or forgotten about me and that it simply was not my time yet. In fact, I told the devil to get behind me and dared him to watch what God was going to do in my life. I then prayed, repented for being mad at God, and cried myself to sleep.

A few months later, another close friend of mine got engaged. Again, I was genuinely ecstatic for her because she is my sister in Christ who had been serving God with me in the ministry. Her fiancé, whom I know well, was an ordained minister and served the Lord with his whole heart. We all had been friends for several years, so I knew this was coming. Even still, in the midst of it all, I found myself asking God, "Why am I still single? I serve you as fervently as she does, so how come you sent her blessing? Where's my Boaz? God, I so desperately want to hang on to your promises, but I don't know how much longer I can wait. Celibacy is hard enough, and now I have to sit back and watch everyone around me get what I'm waiting for. It just seems so unfair God."

One day, in the middle of my Christ-centered journey of serving God, praying for others, and reaping the benefits of kingdom living, I retrieved a message on my voice mail. Some guy with a deep voice, who seemed to know me personally, left a message asking that I return his call. I thought I recognized the voice, so I called him back. After a few minutes into the conversation, I realized I did not know this brother. He started asking me about my parents, about my grandmother, and asked if I was still modeling and doing plus-size fashion shows. As I'm trying to figure out who in the world I was talking to, I decided to ask him his name again. He said "Pep". I said "Oh hi, Pat, how are you doing?" He said "No, Pep". I replied, "Who?" He said "Pep...Pepper" Then I blurted out "Oh my goodness! How have you been?" When I realized who was on the other end of the phone, I was so excited! It had been a few years, and I didn't think our paths would ever cross again. We immediately began talking, reconnecting, and building a friendship. Once we learned that we were both emotionally available, things were looking up. Then, when I learned that he was now saved, worshipping the Lord Jesus, and going to church every Sunday, I knew God had been up to something.

After a few conversations, he asked me if I was interested in seeing how far we could go this time. In seeing how mature he had become, I took a chance and accepted his offer to see how far we could go. Finally, we began officially dating. After many road trips and long weekends filled with boat rides, good ole southern cooking, beaches, and me trying to bait a fishing rod, I was in a place where I was finally enjoying a healthy relationship. Although life was good, I felt like we were just drifting along with no real destination in sight. After about a year and a half, I thought to myself, "What are we doing? Where are we going? I can't be his girlfriend forever! How much longer are we going to date? It'll be hard, but maybe I should end things. I'm not getting any younger so maybe I should move on." Although I was tired of feeling like I was going through the motions of being in a relationship, I just couldn't leave. After all, I loved him and wanted to be with him, just not as his girlfriend anymore. Impatient, tired, and frustrated, I hung in there.

On Sunday, October 12, 2008 (at 10:26 a.m.), on our way to church in Jacksonville, North Carolina, Pepper decided to take a different route to church. He told me he needed to stop at the ATM first. But we had passed two already, and he didn't stop. I emphatically asked "Sweetie, why did you wait until the last minute to go to the ATM? Why didn't you get cash last night while we were out? See, we're going to be late for church. I'm not telling your mom why we're late. You're going to tell her. This is ridiculous." Yadda yadda yadda, off I go, just fussing' about why this and why that. Then I noticed that we were pulling up at the pier we went to on my very first road trip with him two years prior. I still couldn't figure out what he was doing. I asked, but he didn't answer. He pulled into a parking space and turned his truck off. He proceeded to tell me that he had something he wanted to tell me, and that he wanted to tell me to my face before I heard it from someone else. I'm all nervous and almost freaking out and trying to figure out what he was getting ready to tell me. He started sharing and said that lately, he had been lying about where he was whenever I called him. He told me he lied about working late; he lied the week before about being at his brother's house, and he lied about cutting the grass that day when I called. Naturally, I'm scared and am getting ready to protect my emotions because he's about to tell me something really crazy. Immediately, I start thinking, "I know he did not bring me all the way to Jacksonville, NC to tell me he's been cheating, or to tell me he wants out of the relationship or that he's already married. Oh, I know he better not tell me something crazy like he accidentally got somebody pregnant or he's an atheist now." I was scared to hear what would come out of his mouth next.

As he reached behind my seat in the truck, he said, "I know I've been lying to you about a lot of stuff lately, but one thing I didn't lie about is this." Pepper pulls out an ivory colored Jared box! In disbelief, I'm looking at him like he's crazy. He proceeds to get out of the truck, walk around to the passenger side, opened my door and said, "Michele, will you spend the rest of your life with me?" He opened the box and it was the prettiest ring I'd ever seen! I started crying, pushing him in his big ole chest and blurted out, "You better stop playing with me! Are you serious Pepper? No way?! Really?"

He said "Yes Michele, will you marry me?"

More tears rolled down my face, and as I tried to speak, I just leaned in and kissed him. Then, in the midst of the tears and completely blocked nasal passages, I said, "Babe, even though I can't cook like your mom and I don't like poopy diapers, do you still want to marry me?" He told me that he did. Then I followed it with, "Well in that case then, absolutely yes! I will marry you and I'm ready to spend the rest of my life with you!" In a puddle of tears, we kissed, and then went to church. Needless to say, he hadn't lied about where he had been on all those nights. The alleged "lies" were all a part of his plan to confuse me before he proposed.

For the next two days, all I could do was stare at my ring. I absolutely could not believe that I was now an engaged woman. A few days later, during the ride back to DC, I learned that the day before we left for Jacksonville, my sweetie went and got my parents blessing before proposing. He personally met with my mom, both my dads, and my stepmother to ask for their blessing to marry their daughter. It was then that I was reminded, even when things looked bleak, of how I trusted in the Lord and my strength was renewed. I started having flash backs of all the times I wanted to throw in the towel because God wasn't moving fast enough. I began to have a repentant heart about how close I came to giving up on what God promised me, and how I went against the enemy and chose to trust God and take Him at His word. I remembered how impatient and frustrated I had become, until I was gently reminded through His word that there's a great reward for me if I continue doing His will and that I would receive all that He had promised (Hebrews 10:35-36). That's when I knew without a doubt that after all I had been through, God was listening.

During all those emotional ups and downs, tears, fears, and personal storms with struggling to remain celibate, God continually gave me visions and dreams that I could not understand. Although the dreams were crystal clear, they each seemed so contrary to what I was actually living and experiencing in my life. When I was angry and upset that God was blessing others with their mate, I remembered a lucid dream where I had just given birth to a beautiful little girl with a head full of hair. I was in the recovery room and my husband (whose face was blocked out) was holding our newborn daughter while I slept peacefully. When I was confused and feeling impatient after my sister in Christ became engaged, I clearly remembered a dream where my husband and I were in our kitchen cooking dinner together while people were showing up at our new single family home for our first housewarming.

If I can be transparent for a moment, I will admit that I was searching for a man to complete me. Instead, I found Jesus. When I accepted the fact that God was not pleased with the way I was living my life, that's when I immediately vowed that I would practice celibacy until I got married. Although I faced many challenges, through faith in God and constant prayer, I overcame them all. As a result of my obedience, the Lord sent me a God-fearing man who would later become my husband. After seven arduous years, I happily ended my celibacy when I married on October 10, 2009. The Lord has blessed me tremendously. Approximately one year later, in September 2010, our daughter was born. Although we have not acquired our mansion yet, stay tuned, because God is still listening and I know He is not finished with me yet.

God is good to His children and even though we don't deserve it, He somehow proves that He will never renege on His promises. The thing we must remember, but we often forget, is that God's timing is not our timing. When we think He's forgotten us or we ask why it's taking so long, just know that God knows what He's doing and there is a reason for everything He does. That's why it's important to declare God's word when you don't know what else to do. And at the end of the day, "we know that in all things, God works for the good of those who love him and are called according to his purpose" (Romans 8:28). So no matter what storms you go through, remember, your job is to do three things:

(1) Endure until the end

(2) Declare what He promised you through His word and

(3) Never ever give up on God. In spite of what it looks like, in spite of what the enemy tries to tell you, and in spite of what your friends and family might say - remember what God told you. Remember what He showed you. Remember that He will never leave you nor forsake you and always know that the end of a thing is better than the beginning (Eccl 7:8).

Michele D. Rose is a native Washingtonian who recently married in the fall of 2009. After 7 long years of celibacy, God blessed her with a husband. She currently resides in Maryland with her husband and daughter, and dedicates her story to women who are properly waiting on God.

Contact Michele at inhimiam1@hotmail.com

Let Go and Let God
Xiomara Tucker

The alarm sounded for the second time since I pressed the snooze button. I would have given anything to wake up and realize that last night was all a bad dream instead of my cruel reality. My heart is heavy and my mind is numb. The pain in my lower abdomen is intensifying; as the medication that was injected into my system wears off. My vibrant caramel complexion has lost its special glow. Tears filled my weary eyes as I wrapped my arms around my barren womb. It was my hearts desire to be a joyful mother of children. But after enduring a second miscarriage last night; my chances look slim to none.

My first plight with miscarriage happened a little over a year ago. At the end of a frustrating freshman year in college, I was a lonely and confused nineteen year-old. Most of my friends had found there place in life. Some of them continued on the path to achieve a higher education; while others traveled the world chasing their dreams. The friends that made the biggest impression on me were the ones who were fortunate enough to have children. They seemed to be so happy and complete. I wanted to experience the same kind of joy that only a child could bring. All of my life people referred to me as the 'good girl'. I lived by the golden rule, never got into trouble, or experienced half the things most girls my age did. Loneliness blindsided my focus and I took my eyes off of God. His 'time' was taking too long. I decided to take matters into my own hands.

It wasn't long before I began over indulging in alcohol to fill the void of loneliness. Drinking only impaired my judgment. After the poison left my system and my mind was completely sober, I was still childless and my sorrow only deepened. I started seeing a

99

friend of a friend out of desperation. A broken condom led to an unplanned pregnancy. The awkward fling came to an abrupt end. He suddenly wanted nothing more to do with me and especially not our unborn child.

"I'll buy you the latest pair of Nike Air Max, if you get an abortion." I was appalled. "Wow! Really? A pair of sneakers in exchange for terminating the life of an innocent child. Not in this life time." When I refused to comply with his insane request he continued with excuses. "I'm not ready for a baby. I'm trying to finish college." This fling was doomed from the start. I became involved with this guy for all the wrong reasons. He was never someone I would bring home for my parents to meet. Desperation turned into depression as I struggled to accept the fact that I was about to have a child out of wedlock; and I would have to raise this child alone. I was too ashamed to tell my parents because they had taught me better. Asking the church for help was out of the question. Young women who had children out of wedlock were not exactly welcomed with opened arms. I had no choice other then to play the hand that life had dealt me and take things one day at a time.

I miscarried a few weeks later. My doctor explained that miscarriage in the first trimester is not uncommon. The fetus had not developed properly and my body would not support any further development. The grievance process wasn't easy. I had barely come to terms with the fact that I was carrying a child out of wedlock, when I found myself alone in the emergency room because I had miscarried.

All the medical professionals were so encouraging. Hearing them say, "It will happen when the time is right," gave me an inkling of hope. Although I mourned the loss of a child I would never see on earth; I rejoiced because God had saved my child from a devastating life of dysfunction. I asked the Lord for forgiveness, and prayed that he would create in me a clean heart and a right spirit. My faith was strengthened because God had kept me from danger and protected me from disease. Even after I had taken my eyes off of God; He never took His eyes off of me. As I regained my focus on my Lord and Savior I accepted the consequences for my actions. Legally, I was an adult, but I still had childish ways. I was in no position to raise a child, especially not alone. The world glamorizes money, drugs, and sexual immortality, but they fail to show the life altering consequences of such immoral actions.

My desire to have a child was still strong, but my standards had changed tremendously. I longed to have the kind of love described in the Song of Solomon. Before I could experience that kind of love I first needed to find out what love is according to God. 1 Corinthians13: 4-7 (NIV) says, "Love is patient, love is kind. It does not envy, it does not boast, it is not proud. It is not rude, it is not self seeking, it is not easily angered, it keeps no record of wrongs. Love does not delight in evil but rejoices in the truth. It always protects, always hopes, always preserves." I knew beyond the shadow of a doubt that I had found this love in a childhood friend. For the first time in my adult life I had someone who loved and accepted me and my imperfections. Everybody said "he is the one," including a prophetess who spoke God's promises into my life. I was blindsided by the thought of God finally giving me the family I always wanted. My desire to please God was replaced with my desire to fulfill my on selfish desire. I became rebellious, even though I was saved. Spiritual confirmation became a green light. I figured, if we were going to be a family we may as well start acting like one. My boyfriend and I decided to take our relationship to the next level and moved in together, after nearly a year of dating. We were nervous and excited about starting our family. My parents did not approve of me living with a man before marriage, but they continued to love me anyhow.

"I'm too young to be married. We are going to get married when the time is right." I wanted so badly to justify my actions. "Monogamy is practically matrimony in this day in age. Marriage is just a piece of paper." I listened to ungodly counsel and became distant from God. I thought I had proved everybody wrong when my pregnancy test came up positive a few months later. Everything seemed to be going in the right direction until the pregnancy ended in miscarriage.

"Trust God. All I can tell you to do is to trust God." The words of last nights attending physician echoed like a war cry on the battlefield of my mind. He seemed to be so confident in his faith. I use to be sound in my faith, but doubt was beginning to set in after my life's most recent turn of events. Talking to God was the furthest thing from my mind at the moment. As a child I often heard my Grandmother say, "Don't question God. His ways are not our ways. There is a reason for everything that He does. Sometimes He will take us through things in order to teach us a lesson. You will live and you will learn." What could I possibly learn from this atrocious experience? My faith was dwindling fast. Everything was backwards. Good things were happening to bad people. Bad things kept happening to me, the 'good girl'.

The blaring voice of a television announcer jolted me out of my internal pity party. "Someone out there is hurting. God wants to wipe away every single one of your tears. All you have to do is give your life to Christ Jesus. Call us today. Operators are standing by waiting and ready to pray for you. Matthew 21:22 says, 'And all things whatsoever ye ask in prayer believing, ye shall receive'."

"That's not true!" I shouted at the gray haired man on the television screen as if he could here me. There was no way that I was going to listen to another minute of the false hope coming from that television evangelist who probably had been born with a silver spoon in his mouth. I had asked, I prayed, I even begged for God to bless me with a child. He kept snatching my dream away before it ever became my reality.

I frantically searched for the remote. Just as I was about to turn the power switch the evangelist's tone changed. It seemed as if he was speaking directly to me. "There is a young woman out there who's experiencing some abdominal pain. I am the Lord that healeth thee (Exodus 15:26). God wants to heal you. Don't wait another minute. Pick up the phone and call us today." I dialed the number at the bottom of the screen and closed my eyes as I waited for a live intercessor to come on the line.

"Thank you for calling the Intercessory Prayer Line. How may I pray for you today?"

The warm voice of the telephone operator calmed my uneasiness. "Yes, I was watching the broadcast today. I would like prayer for the healing of my body and to be made whole again. I am experiencing a lot of abdominal pain. The doctor's can't find anything wrong. But there must be something wrong because I just endured a second miscarriage in a little over a year. Why does this keep happening to me?" Tears filled my eyes and streamed down my high cheek bones like a waterfall.

The operator spoke softly as I tried to pull myself together. "I'm sorry for your loss. God's ways are higher than our ways. There is a reason for everything that He does. Is your husband at home? I would like to pray with both of you."

"I'm not married!" Why on earth did she think I was married? Since when do you have to be married to have a child?

103

"You mean to tell me you had two babies out of wedlock?" Her tone went from caring to persecuting.

"No, no, weren't you listening? I didn't have a baby. I had a miscarriage." I struggled to control the sobs that arose from my quivering throat.

"I'm sorry honey, please forgive me for letting my emotions speak for me. I assumed you were married because you seemed to have been on the right track. Do you know what the Bible says about fornication?"

"Yes ma'am, but everyone else is doing it. Most of my friends have children out of wedlock. None of them miscarried. What makes me so different? What did I do to deserve this?"

"Losing your baby is not about what you have done. God allowed Satan to tempt his faithful servant Job. Even after Job lost everything he continued to trust God. Job received double for his trouble, because of his faithfulness. I know you are hurting right now. But I hope you can find comfort in knowing that when God takes something from your grasp; He is not punishing you. He is opening up your hands to receive something greater.

You said most of your friends had children out of wedlock. Everything that looks good is not always good for you. His plan for them is not the same as his plan for you. 1Peter 2:9 says that "We are a chosen generation, a royal priesthood, a holy nation, a peculiar people." You were not created to be like everybody else. God said that we should be holy for He is holy. He hears your cries, and He knows everything you have need of even before you ask. God wants to give you so much more than just a baby."

"Psalms 84:11 says, not one good thing will He withhold from those who do what is right. Flowers need rain in order to grow. Sometimes we must go through the rain in order to blossom into the beautiful creation that God designed us to be. Weeping may endure for a night. But joy will come in the morning light. God will never put more on you than you can bear. I am not just quoting scriptures. I'm speaking from my own life experiences. I apologize for being so blunt. I'm speaking out of love. God corrects those that He loves. I am not casting judgment but showing you the error of your ways so that you can repent of your sins and come back to the path of righteousness. As long as you have breath in your body you have a chance to make things right with God."

My first thought was, if God will never put more on me than I can bear, He must have me confused with someone else. Then I realized I must be some kind of strong to have endured not one but two untimely miscarriages. The fact that I am still alive, and in my right mind, means that I am stronger than I ever thought I could be. The words of a gospel song 'Be Encouraged' by William Becton ministered to my wounded soul. God would make everything right, but I had to stay strong and keep holding on.

Living by the book hadn't been so bad after all. I stumbled and fell the moment I stepped out of the Will of God. Even though I was spiritually wounded I was able to get back up and walk again. This time God would lead and I would follow. I thought I was missing out on all the fun and games. All I got was sorrow and pain. There is a lot more to life than the sins the world glorifies.

This conversation was the turning point in my young adult life. God used this woman to speak life, wisdom, love and understanding to my lost soul. I heard the Lord speak to me. He said, "Stop my child. You are going the wrong way. Come back to me. You need me to survive. Be still and know that I am God. I know what's best for you. I have plans to prosper and not to harm you. I provide for the birds in the air. Surely I will provide for you. To everything there is a season and a time for every purpose under the heaven." I thought I had gone too far and it was no use turning back. She showed me that, nothing can separate me from the love of God.

The telephone operator prayed with me. I heard the heavens rejoice as I rededicated my life to Christ. My stumbling block was transformed into a stepping stone. This transition reminded me of the Parable of the Lost Sheep. Jesus spoke of a shepherd who had one hundred sheep. One of the sheep wandered away while the sheep were grazing in the pasture. The shepherd left the ninety-nine sheep in the pasture and searched for that one. He rejoiced when he found that one. The same is with our Father in heaven. Jesus said, "There will be more joy in heaven over one sinner who repents than over ninety-nine respectable people who do not need to repent" (Luke 15:7).

I could not wait to share the news of the new journey my life was about to begin. My boyfriend was very receptive to my new outlook on life. I told him all about the conversation I had with the telephone operator. We prayed together and confessed our sins before God. Playing house wasn't worth the unforeseen consequences. The pain that had been brought upon us was something we never wanted to face again. God created us in His own image. He had been so gracious to give us life and let us find each other. It was time that we honored God with our whole hearts. My boyfriend proposed to me out of the unconditional love he had for me, and the reverence he had for Almighty God. I accepted. Not because I thought it would increase my chances of getting pregnant; but because I knew he was my Adam and I was his Eve. We agreed to take our time and seek premarital counseling before we took the final step. The wedding date was set for the spring of the following year.

One week later, I returned to my job as a nurturing preschool teacher, in a prestigious part of town. Smiling faces and warm hugs from all the little children eased my pain. I felt like I was back where I belonged. But it became hard to control my feelings of inadequacy as my work day neared its end. Parents of all ages and different races came to take their precious children home with them. Seeing the joy on the parent's faces when they came to pick up their little one was like pouring salt onto an open wound. Conflicting questions arose in my mind each time a parent entered the classroom. "Why did God give her a child? She is more focused on her career than her child. I give these children my undivided attention and love every single day." "Why did they wait so late to have children?" I thought when an older couple came into the room. "They look more like grandparents than parents. I still have plenty of energy. I bet they just sit around and do nothing at home." "She is clueless when it comes to parenting. I taught her child everything she knows." This fiasco of questioning continued until the last child left to go home.

I was handed a card as I walked the last child to the door. The middle aged mother hugged me tightly and assured me that every thing was going to be alright. Her words were sincere as if she could read the ill thoughts in my mind. I retreated to my desk and opened what I thought was just another sympathy card. On the outside of the card was the cutest picture of a duck using one of its wings to protect a helpless little mouse from the rain. The inscription on the card read, "God never meant for us to face tough times alone... That's why He gave us each other." She added a personal message at the bottom which said, "I was so sad to hear about your miscarriage. It breaks my heart and reminds me of the two I had before I had John. You are in my prayers! Take care of yourself and God Bless."

Her kindness brought me great comfort and rekindled my faith. If God made a way for her I knew he could do the same for me. She was living proof that God could make the seemingly impossible become a reality. For the first time I realized that I was not alone. God was not picking on me. He had not allowed anything to happen to me that hadn't already happened to others. The Bible says there is nothing new under the heavens. There are numerous accounts of biblical women who struggled with infertility. I began studying their stories to see how they kept their faith while they waited on God to fulfill his promise in their lives. Sarah, Hannah and Elizabeth were three amazing women whose stories stuck out in my mind. In time God allowed each of them to bare children.

Sarah the wife of Abraham struggled with infertility for years. God told them that Abraham would be the father of many nations. I believe Sarah had grown tired of waiting for the words that God had spoken to manifest. She offered her maidservant Hagar to sleep with her husband Abraham. Sarah thought she would be happy if Hagar had a child for her. Hagar became proud and despised Sarah when she became pregnant with Abraham's child. Sarah felt more inadequate and resentful than she had before. She eventually had Hagar and her son Ishmael sent away. Sarah was living in condemnation. I believe Hagar was a constant reminder of the mess Sarah caused after restlessly waiting on God. I felt Sarah's pain. Time went on and Sarah remained childless. One day God spoke to Abraham and told him that his wife would bare a child in old age. Abraham questioned his fate. God said, "Is there anything to hard for the Lord (Genesis 18:14)?" My faith was again strengthened. Nothing is too hard for God. Sarah laughed when she heard the news that she would bare a child in old age. Abraham was one hundred years old and Sarah was ninety years old when God fulfilled his promise. Sarah gave birth to a son, she named Isaac.

I was still young. That gave the Lord plenty of time to fulfill his promise in my life. I decided to wait on the Lord. Even if that meant I would not conceive a child until I was well out of my prime. I hoped it wouldn't take that long. But any way the Lord blessed me I was going to be satisfied. Sarah's story taught me that God is in control. I used to think some people purposefully waited until they were old to have children. Now I realize that it was God who allowed them to have children in their old age.

Hannah was a righteous woman who struggled with infertility. Her husband Elkanah had two wives. To make matters worse Peninnah, Elkanah's other wife had children. Peninnah made fun of Hannah's barren womb. Hannah became so upset by Peninnah's ridicule that she refused to eat. 1Samuel 1:9-10 says that she was deeply distressed, and she cried bitterly as she prayed to the Lord. She promised the Lord that she would dedicate her child back to the Lord if he would grant her request. Hannah prayed so long and hard until there was no sound coming from her moving lips. Eli the High Priest accused her of being a drunken mess. She explained that she was not drunk but praying out of desperation and despair. Eli heard her pain and told her to go in peace, that God may grant her request. She went away with her husband and Lord answered her prayer. Hannah birthed a son. She named him Samuel. The name Samuel means, "I asked the Lord for him." As soon as Samuel was weaned, Hannah dedicated him back to the Lord just as she had promised.

My faith was on fire after I read Hannah's story. Hannah's infertility was only temporary. God had an appointed time and purpose for her son Samuel. If he had been born earlier he would not have been able to fulfill the purpose that God intended for his life. After Hannah had done all she knew how to do, she went forward in peace. The faith that had dwindled down to the size of a mustard seed had taken root and was beginning to blossom into the vastness of a tree. It was time for me to move forward in peace. I waited in expectation because I knew God had heard my prayer; and, I believed he would answer.

Elizabeth was an upright woman in the sight of the Lord. She and her husband Zechariah lived good lives and fully obeyed the Lord's laws and commandments. They had no children because Elizabeth's womb was barren. She and her husband were very old. One day while Zechariah was working in the temple, Gabriel, an angel of the Lord appeared to him. Gabriel told Zechariah that God had heard his prayer and his wife Elizabeth would bare a son whom they were to name John. Gabriel said that John, the Baptist would bring much happiness to them and everyone surrounding them.

Zechariah doubted the prophetic word spoken by Gabriel because he and his wife were in old age. Gabriel caused Zechariah to become mute until the day God's promise came to pass because he did not believe. Elizabeth became pregnant sometime later. She praised God for helping her because she no longer felt like a public disgrace. Her praise came months before the baby was born. Faith allowed her to praise God in advance for the miracle she knew was coming. Everyone rejoiced when the baby was born because God had been so good to his faithful servants.

Elizabeth had a heart of contentment. Not once in the Bible did it speak of Elizabeth complaining or being distressed because of her barrenness. When she spoke it was to praise God. All I had done was complain and worry about why, how and when things were going to change in my life. Again I heard God speak, "Don't worry about tomorrow, focus on today. My grace is sufficient."

Pray about everything and worry about nothing. Hold on, keep the faith. Your dreams will come to pass."

I knew that faith was the substance of things hoped for and the evidence of things not seen (Hebrews11:1). But I didn't quiet understand what it meant to 'keep the faith'. My mother directed me to the book of Hebrews, chapter eleven. This chapter is filled with countless acts of faith. Believers were able to see God's promises come to pass in their lives. Reading this chapter allowed me to see that faith without works is dead. There is a worldly saying, "Put your money where your mouth is." It was time for me to put my faith where my mouth was. There was no more time for worrying, complaining, or trying to do things on my own. I stepped out on faith.

Marriage was a big step in the right direction. Most people believe marriage is a special bond between a man and a woman. Premarital counseling taught us that a successful marriage consists of a man, a woman, and God. Good looks and sweet words fade over time. God never changes and his love never fails. Our focus was to please God by loving and honoring one another. After about a month of living in marital bliss the newness seemed to fade. I was more then happy to be surrounded by the love of God and my devoted husband, but something was not right. Someone once told me that marriage was another job within it self. All of my energy was drained. My emotions were spiraling out of control. I consulted with my doctor to see if he could prescribe me some vitamin supplements that would give me more energy.

I was beyond ecstatic when the doctor prescribed a twelve month supply of prenatal vitamins. God answered my prayer. The tiny miracle growing on the inside of me was draining all my energy and altering my emotions. I laughed like Sarah laughed, prayed like Hannah and praised the Lord like Elizabeth. Nine months later my life long dream became my reality. All the pain from my past became a distant memory; as, I stared into the dreamy eyes of my first born son. The Lord is faithful and just to forgive us of ours sins and cleanse us from all unrighteousness (1John1:9). The birth of our son was only the beginning of the goodness God had in store for us. The Bible says that God will give us double for our troubles. He has blessed our union with three wonderful children. Each of them brings us unexplainable joy. They are a constant reminder of how great God is. Those traumatic events took place in my life more then a decade ago. God brought me through each test and trial in order to birth a triumphant testimony.

Xiomara L. Tucker resides in Charlotte, North Carolina with her husband and three wonderful children. This story is dedicated to all women who have struggled with infertility in the natural and spiritual realms. She is currently working on her first Christian Fiction Novel to be released the summer of 2011. Contact Xiomara at: tuckerxiomara@yahoo.com

Forgiveness is For Real
Martha Lee

When I was fifteen years old, I witnessed my then boyfriend, Calvin, go after a man and try to kill him because the man was arguing with his mother. Calvin stood in his mom's yard arguing with the man. He went into his mom's kitchen to get a long butcher knife and then charged down the alley towards the man. Calvin's mother ran after him, trying to stop his murderous rage. When the man was within reach, Calvin raised his arm, ready to stab the man. But his mother threw up her arm to keep her son from stabbing the man. He then stabbed his mom in her arm, pulled the knife out, pushed her over to me and told me to take care of her. Oh my goodness, he stabbed her through and through and then pulled out the knife. He proceeded toward the man. The man bent over and Calvin stabbed him in the back so hard he couldn't get the knife out, so he broke it off. The man fell down on the ground. Then Calvin proceeded to hit him in the head with a thick piece of wood. This man's head moved back and forth as Calvin continued to hit him. I thought the man was dead. The police came.

They locked Calvin up, took the man and Calvin's mom to the hospital. I was so shocked I did not know what to do. What I should have done was run back home and never see this man again, right? Many of you will be surprised to know that I kept right on seeing that crazy maniac. I was young, impressionable and I had no direction for my life. So, I was swept into a life of misery and destruction. I tell this story now, for all the young girls that are going astray. Stop and listen… my fate doesn't have to be your fate.

During the court case, Calvin's mother told the judge that the neighbor stabbed her and that her son was just protecting her. How could they lie like this? The judge asked the man, what happened?

The man replied, "I was arguing with this lady, and the next thing I knew her son showed up. I was talking to him, discussing what his mom and I were in disagreement about. He pulled a butcher knife on me and chased me down the alley. I bent down and someone stabbed me, I fell down on the ground and all I remember after that is, someone hitting me on my head with something. I do not know what he used to hit me with because I blacked out.

The judge then asked Calvin if he had hit the man.

Calvin said, "Yes." Then the judge asked, with what weapon? Calvin said "I didn't use a weapon to hit him. I used these." He held up his two fists. The people in the courtroom laughed and the judge dismissed the case. I was shocked. The judge never even asked Calvin if he had stabbed the man.

No long after that, Calvin and I got married. I was so convinced that Calvin loved me and wanted to marry me, that I packed my bags and ran away to be with him. I was only sixteen at the time, but I thought I was grown because I could now stay out as late as I wanted. I could say anything to anybody. My mom was devastated. My father talked to Calvin and told him he would kill him if he ever hurt me. They relented and finally gave me permission by signing the papers.

Calvin's grandmother was very old but she was active in her church and invited her family to attend often. I went sometimes but I knew nothing about salvation whatsoever. While living with his family I saw many things that made me wonder about how they were raised. His brothers were criminals. They were thieves and went to jail often. As a matter of fact, none of the sons were home at the same time. One was always in jail for some crime. When the family got together, they honored these men instead of telling them they were wrong. In order to fit in I acted just like them and went with the flow.

Calvin went to jail many times for many reasons. The main crime he was locked up for was rape. But he never got any real time for it. This baffled me. I wondered why he wasn't in jail. He always reminded me that these women were lying on him and the reason they had him locked up was because he didn't want them. I wasn't used to living like this. I had to go and visit him because no one else went, ever. One day I packed my clothes and went back home, hoping my mother would welcome me back immediately with open arms. But she didn't. I guess she was hurt about me running away, so I had to choose between staying home and becoming a child all over again or going back to Calvin's mom's house and not taking instructions from anyone but me. Being young minded, I went back to Calvin's house

I had never been involved with a convict, so I thought he was telling the truth when he said he didn't do those crimes. He was accused of raping my mother's next door neighbor with a stocking cap on and didn't get any time for that. He kept being found not guilty. Another woman he had been accused of raping had been my friend. But I believed him once again.

Time went on. His sister and I did not get along so we left his mom's house and went to live with his aunt. She did not have room for us, so we slept on her couch. I missed my very own bed back at my mom's house. He didn't want me to work so I didn't. It's not like I had any skills. I had dropped out of high school after passing to the twelfth grade. Calvin was a good provider but he treated me like I was his property, not his wife. I had to make sure everything was done the exact the way he wanted it. I was afraid of him.

One day while we were visiting my mother, I went to the store to get something. My mom was on the couch asleep. When I came back my sister was screaming my name. She came downstairs following my husband who had blood running from his baby finger. It looked like it had been filet. I asked what happened. My sister came over to me with the knife still in her hand and said, "Your husband tried to rape me." Calvin denied it, and although I did not admit it out loud, I blamed myself for this.

To this day, I want to write a letter to my sister in the sky and say I am sorry. I was so young and confused I didn't understand why he tried to do this my sister.

But he raped me too. I was expecting our son at the time. Calvin wanted to have sex with me. But we were waiting for a bus to take us to Atlantic City. It was a preplanned trip and we had tickets along with twenty other people. There wasn't any place to be intimate at all. I explained this fact to him. He asked me to travel with him through this alley for a minute. Then in the middle of the walk he lowered me down on top of this mound of glass and had his way with me. I was so ashamed but too afraid to resist. This was the worse thing he could have done to me especially while I was pregnant.

Calvin also attempted to rape an eight year old little girl. The little girl got away before he could do anything to her, thank God. But the raping didn't stop. As a matter of fact, during our ten year marriage Calvin went back and forth to jail so many times he was in jail more times than he was home with me and his children. The last time he got locked up, it was for the rape of the next door neighbor of his then girlfriend. I no longer wanted to be married to him and I thought to myself, this is my opportunity to finally get away from him. I heard the state had a very strong case against him, and without a doubt he was going to prison. I decided to attend this trial. He got five years for the crime. Calvin's lawyer offered to be my lawyer in case I wanted to divorce him because the courts had plenty of evidence of adultery and since he was found guilty of this charge I would have no problems at all. So, I divorced him.

I had moved on with my life, hoping to never see Calvin again. But that wasn't to be. I was asleep in my bed when I suddenly awoke from my nap. My boyfriend at the time, we'll call him (Megal), came to me and said, "Your ex-husband called."

All of my senses were alert. I asked, "What did he want?"

"Oh, he said something like, let me speak to my wife. I told him you were asleep. Then he wanted to talk to the kids. I told him they were out playing and then he told me that he was on his way to see them. And that he was going to deal with me when he gets here."

"Go get something to defend yourself with," I told him, because I knew that Calvin was going to do exactly what he said. Megal left and I was left there to face, Calvin on my own. I got up and prepared myself for whatever would come. Within an hour, there was a knock at the door. It was Calvin. After all the things I saw him do to other people, I was very terrified of him. So, when he asked me to open the door, I emphatically said, "No!"

He began to argue with me and demanded to come in to see his kids. I still said, no. I knew this man, and I knew he had a gun or some type of weapon on him. He never fought fair with anyone, ever. Thank God I had double bolted locks on my door. They were the strong ones that required a key to enter or exit.

My children were in the same room, peeping out of the window behind the curtain. When I noticed this, I told them to get

117

out of the window and go to bed. I finally, told him that I was not going to talk to him anymore. So I put the screen down on the window and started to turn around. It was then that I saw him reach behind his back and pull out a gun. He placed it in the palm of his hand with his finger on the trigger and then supported it as he sprayed bullets at me through the screen in my second floor window. The screen was the only obstacle between me and this array of bullets. Suddenly I began to wonder what was happening to me and why. I glanced through the window looking for Megal's return. Then I felt this GREAT burning sensation. It was then that I realized I had been shot.

I started bleeding profusely from my back and under my right arm. I called the police over and over again. Oh my goodness where was the police when I needed them? After eight voice messages someone finally answered, I told the man I had been shot by my ex-husband and that he was outside of my home right now. By this time my block was filled with people who were responding to my yells for help. Finally the police came. I was able to tell them just who did this and where he lived and apparently that was where he went after he finished shooting at me. The police helicopter arrived just as he was getting out of his cab. They locked him up right away.

As I got into the ambulance, I was devastated. I was bleeding, in pain and feeling as if I was going to die. At that moment, I knew I had to get right with God, because I was a backslider. The paramedics kept telling me to keep still and lay down flat. I told them, "It hurts bad," But it did not seem to matter to them. When I got to the hospital the attending physician said I had a bullet lodged in my back above my right shoulder blade and it needed to be removed. The doctor determined that the bullet was from a 22 and the bullet had been filled down. The purpose of this was so the

118

bullet would explode on impact. He said it was a good thing that I was standing sideways when he shot me because the bullet entered through my right underarm and lodged at my shoulder blade. Otherwise, if it had hit me straight on, it would have exploded on impact, leaving me with no shoulder or worse. It could have taken the right side of my upper body off and I would have died.

After being released from the hospital, I went home. When I reached my bedroom, I began to relive the shooting all over again. The holes in the wall were so big that I could put my hand in each of them and turn it around as if a large bullet had done the damage. It was not until then that I realized what the doctor meant when he said that this little bullet could not do such massive damage unless it had been filed down thereby causing an exploding effect upon impact. Years ago, Calvin had told me that I belonged to him and that he'd kill me before letting me go. I was so afraid and full of fear from this man. I wondered if he was going to be released this time as he had been so many times in the past.

As I sat down in my living room thoughts began to enter my mind about how happy I had been when I had given my life to God a few years ago. I even let my mind go back to when I first went to church. See I had backslid and was living a sinful life. I began to remember how nice my life had been when I went to church and how I'd wanted to do what was right in the eyes of God. The scriptures told me that the battle was not mine, but it belonged to the Lord. I began to relax and then I gave my heart to the lord right then.

The Lord helped me to realize that Calvin was just a bully and his fear tactics were not going work on me anymore. So I did not worry about him harming me. I prayed about the upcoming court case and I believed that God would make sure that this man couldn't hurt anyone else. When it was all said and done, Calvin was sentenced to thirty-five years. He received twenty-five of those years for trying to kill me and ten more for setting his girlfriend's home on fire.

Calvin did not complete his sentence. He was released after twenty-five years. At first I thought the system had failed me and his other victims again, but then I learned that Calvin had been released because he was ill and only had about a year to live. Calvin had moved in with my daughter because he had no where else to go.

I vividly remember how I came to forgive him for what he had done. I was reading my Bible and thanking God for the joy of my salvation when my thought was interrupted as a small voice in my head had said, "You have to forgive Calvin for what he did to you just as Christ forgave you for your sins when he died on the cross."

Well I said to myself, "Now where did that come from?" Surely it could not be the Lord saying this. After all, I had a right to resent Calvin. He tried to kill me. I was justified in not liking this person. But the voice repeated the same thing as before. It was then that I realized that this was something I had to do in order to make heaven my home. The Bible is very clear on forgiving and unless you forgive others for what they have done to you then Christ won't forgive you for what you have done to others. I got down on my knees and cried like a baby. I had stored up a lot of hate for this man. I had given him ten years of my life, not to mention the three kids we had together. He had hurt me and my family in many ways. The tears wouldn't stop as I thought of the pain he had caused me and my family. But then I got this warm feeling all over me as all of the hate was being pulled out of my gut and I was being filled with this wonderful ability to forgive.

One day, I was on my way home from work and my cell phone rang. It was my daughter. She sounded rather scared, so I asked her what was wrong. She asked if I could just pray for her. So, I began to pray and when I had finished, she told me that her dad had been laying on the couch for three days and not eating. She was afraid that he was dying. Then she asked me to come over to her house and pray for him. I agreed to go, but as I hung up my phone all sorts of thoughts went through my mind. I wondered if he was just saying that he was sick to finally get me over there and finish the job he started. I imagined that my daughter was trying to help her father kill me. I realize that those thoughts were irrational now, but fear had gripped me and my mind was working overtime.

But I came to realize that fear is just (FALSE EVIDENCE APPEARING REAL). The Bible tells us that we are not to be fearful of anything, for God did not give us (his children) the spirit of fear, but love, peace and a sound mind. For years, I had told myself that I wasn't afraid of Calvin anymore. I had the truth of the Bible on my side and I didn't need to fear any man. But that was when I didn't have to be in his presence.

I thought that I had forgiven Calvin, but the moment I told my daughter that I would come to her house and pray for him, fear paralyzed me. I called one of my Christian sisters and told her about the request and asked her to pray for Calvin. She said, "I need to pray for you after everything you told me about him." That simple comment brought about more anxiety. Because my friend was right; Calvin was a monster and I had no business going near him. But I also knew that Calvin needed prayer and it was my duty as a blood bought Christian to pray for any and everyone in need of prayer.

I thought about Andrew, a fellow minister at my church. I called Andrew and asked him to meet me at my daughter's house to pray for Calvin. He agreed. Then I called my brother and asked him to meet us over there also. The bible says one can put a thousand to flight but two can put ten thousand to flight, so I figured that the three of us should be able to get rid of all two hundred million or so, of Calvin's demons.

I arrived at my daughter's house. Then I looked for her father. I spied him over on the couch and I did not recognize him. He looked like he was dead already. He was a bag of bones. HIS face was unshaven and when I touched his arm he said ouch, so I knew he was fragile. When I saw him, I literally cried. He looked weak and very frail. I prayed for him immediately. That is when I felt true forgiveness for him. As I sat beside him, none of the things he did to me when we were together came to my mind. I saw him as a soul that needed rescuing by the Holy Ghost. When he opened his eyes and saw me, he asked me to forgive him for everything. I said to him, "I already have."

He smiled. Wow, I was relieved when he started to show some sign life. Thank God. Even though he was weak and fragile, I knew he needed hear about Christ and his power not only to heal but to save as well. A grabbed his hand I asked him if he was ready to meet his maker. He said I then asked him if he wanted to receive Jesus as his savior so he could go heaven when he left this world. He said yes. By this time my brother arrived. My daughter, my brother, his wife and I, all stood up and join hands. We all agreed with him in prayer. I saw tears of joy coming down face. It was wonderful. Calvin said he wished he had our marriage to over. He also said he was sorry he had served the devil and missed out o wonderful life with me and Jesus. We talked about some of the go memories from when we were together. Then I asked him if he remember some of those songs he taught me when we were together. He said sure. A as we sang and went down memory lane, he seemed to get stronger.

Listen to me. There is nothing worth holding a grudge over. It can weigh you down worse than a two ton elephant. I visited him two more times before he passed away.

Once again my daughter called me when I was on my way home from work. She said, "This is my daddy's last day on earth, so can you please come see him?" I heard the pain in my daughter's voice, and new that this was important to her, so I went. But Calvin had already gone home to glory by the time I arrived. He looked like he was asleep. He looked better in death than he did in life.

Proverbs3: 5-6, "Trust in the Lord with all your heart, lean not to your own understanding. In all your ways acknowledge Him and He shall direct your path." Heed my testimony, and never go astray. My prayer is that you always let the Lord lead and guide you down the path He has designed for you. But if you should fall off His path, then I pray that you have enough faith to turn back. He is able to heal and restore.

Listening Ear
Serena T. Wills

When you go through deep waters and great trouble, I will be with you. When you go through rivers of difficulty, you will not drown. When you walk through the fire of oppression, you will not be burned up—the flames will not consume you. For I am the Lord your God, your Savior, the Holy One of Israel...Don't be afraid, for I am with you. Isaiah 43:2, 3, 5, TLB

On February 19th, 2010 at 7:42 p.m. I lost my best friend and spiritual leader...my mother, Marguerite "Sauti" Wills. The battle with ovarian cancer was no longer hers as she took her last breath with me and my cousin Fern at her side. In that moment I felt the peace and serenity of God in the hospital room as He took over my mother's pain and solidified my faith as she passed away.

I think back to when I was raised a devout Catholic and was made to go to church every Sunday for nearly sixteen years of my life with my grandparents. I even attended catholic school for three years before my mother pulled me out and transferred me into a public school. My faith wasn't mine. It was forced on me so I ended up straying away from the church for nearly thirteen years. I prayed and went to church on holidays but that was all I did.

In 2004, I felt emptiness like I had never felt before. I was at the end of a turbulent relationship with my boyfriend at that time and I knew I had to return to my faith and find a church home. Praying and meditating more every day, I asked God to lead me to a place that would speak to me; somewhere I could fellowship with likeminded Christians and hear the word. After numerous visits around the Washington DC area, I found my home at Ebenezer AME (African Methodist Episcopal) Church in Ft.

Washington, Maryland. The title of the first sermon delivered by Co-Pastor Reverend Dr. Joann Browning was, "Keep Your Head Up."

Ever since that day I've never looked back. On March 13, 2005 I gave my life to the Lord. I should be strapped down in a mental institution or should have even committed suicide with this tragedy of losing mom. However my faith that was restored in 2005 has prevented me from even having the slightest thoughts of going crazy, feeling completely broken and totally lost. I never thought I could live life without my mother at such a young age.

But I need to back up, in January of 2009, after turning thirty-four years old, my job in Dallas, Texas where I relocated took a sharp turn. Only one week after I witnessed the greatest piece of American history, watching the inauguration of President Barack Obama and had a feeling of encouragement, I was told that my position would drastically change. Although I heard words coming out of the mouths of management I heard another, a greater one say, "You need to leave."

At first I didn't comprehend the words as I thought the powerful voice was simply telling me to leave the room. But the words became clearer and more defined when one of the higher ups said, "Your job will change as of July 1st, you won't have the same responsibilities working in the community; instead you will be managing one of our after school programs. Your manager will also change effective that date as well. Do you have any final thoughts or questions?"

Although I had some ungodly things to say, as that was a demotion for me as I managed after school programs in 1997 and was hoping my next position would be my manager's job. My work in the community would shift greatly to a point that I didn't like as well. I recited to myself, "Let the words of my mouth and the meditation of my heart be acceptable in thy sight, my strength and my Redeemer."

It was that moment the voice no one else could hear grew a little louder and said, "Your time is up in Dallas, TX and you need to leave."

I told them, "I have to think about my decision and pray on my next steps." Excusing myself from the cold conference room I felt God at my side—I know He counseled me through that session. My long strides down the hallway to my cubicle defined the type of woman I have come to be, always holding my head up high despite the circumstances.

I didn't know my next steps would be filled with a journey that I wasn't ready to take until it was given to me. I finally got back to my desk and called my mother. Mom was a tad bit upset and she softly advised, "Serena...come back east where you belong, come home."

Being in Dallas for over three years was a blessing and I didn't regret moving there. Despite moving for love and living with my boyfriend I had come into my own, moved out and realized after a while that God moved me not for him, but to help me regain focus on my writing. Not only did I pour my energy into my gift but I was now a published author. After I focused and realized my true gifts, I felt the shift and knew that it was God telling me, "It's time to leave and go home."

Over the next few weeks I fasted and prayed. I asked my prayer partners to pray for guidance for me and as much as they didn't want me to leave, they obeyed His word and asked God just for that. I resigned from my job at the beginning of March.

I steadily packed and even joined a spiritual growth class at Oak Cliff Bible Fellowship in Dallas during my last few months. Throughout the class I gained a deeper understanding of the Word and how to quiet my spirit and listen to God. I told my new friends that I had to move back east. They each agreed that it was the word of God and to go. There were some naysayers who said I needed to stay. Since my writing was taking off they thought this was a *bad* move. I'm so thankful that I listened to God and moved forward. If I lost them as friends then they weren't meant to be in my life anyway.

So on July 8, 2009, I left Dallas, TX and moved back to Alexandria, Virginia. When I pulled into Virginia I called my mother and I heard excitement in her voice. Even though I was a four hour train ride/drive from Queens, New York, where she resided, I was still 20 hours closer to her than I had been for the past three and a half years.

I was happy that we would finally have our date to the doctor as I promised her before I moved back east. My mom hadn't been feeling well, but she was fearful of doctors. So, the only way she would go to the doctor was if I went with her. The year prior in the fall of 2008 she admitted to me that she was afraid to go because of what they *would* find. I brushed it off and told her, "What do you mean what they *will* find? How do you know? Mom it's better to know than to not know…right? "

Wrong! She didn't go in 2008 but I didn't give up hope or faith and knew that it was smooth sailing now that I was home. I had taken the trip to New York that Friday July 17th to attend my high school reunion. The bus ride that should have taken four hours took six hours. Traffic was backed up on I-95 North and I was anxious to see my family. When I arrived in Manhattan and called my mother she asked me to stay with friends until Sunday. She said, "It doesn't make sense for you to come into Queens to go right back into the city all weekend, I'll see you Sunday." I listened to her even though I didn't comprehend why she didn't want to see me yet.

On Sunday, I arrived at my mom and grandmother's house at 4:00 p.m. Anxiously placing my key into the front door, I swung it open and said, "Hello...I'm home, Ma!" After closing the front door and walking into the living room I found my mother sound asleep in her favorite recliner. When I knelt down to kiss her on the forehead she slowly stirred awake. When she opened her eyes she smiled weakly and said just above a whisper, "Hi...you're home."

It wasn't like my mother to nap in the middle of the day. I noticed she barely touched her bowl of soup on the coffee table and seemed extremely drained. I cleaned up the coffee table and got her something else to eat. Afterwards I greeted my sister, Christina with a big hug and then went upstairs and sat with my grandmother (Nana). The worry in Nana's eyes will remain imprinted in my memory forever. Nana pleaded, "You have to get your mother to the doctor. There's something wrong, I can feel it."

I smiled, trying to remain strong, "Nana I'm home now and I'll take her. She'll be fine." I don't think I convinced Nana, she replied weakly, "Okay dear, I'm just so worried, but I'm glad you're closer to home. Now we can get some answers."

The answers came sooner than expected. On August 4th, I was standing on the platform of the metro station in Takoma Park, Maryland. I had just turned my phone back on after a job interview when I received an alarming message from Nana. Instead of calling her back I decided to call my mother because I usually handled bad news better coming from her than I did when it came from Nana. After several rings mom didn't answer.

When I didn't reach mom, I went ahead and called Nana. The first thing she said was, "It's your mom; she went to the hospital.

She had trouble breathing and hasn't had a bowel movement in over three weeks."

I said, "Excuse me...three weeks? She didn't tell me this!"

Nana said, "Please get to New York."

I hung up the phone and a woman on the platform touched my arm and said, "Are you okay?"

Answering her with tears in my eyes, "No I'm not, my mother is in the hospital and I have to get to her. She's in New York."

The woman said, "I don't know you but I will start praying for you."

I replied, "Thank you."

I obeyed Nana's request and two days later my friend Renee picked me up from my apartment in Alexandria, Virginia and we drove up I-95 North to Queens, so I could be with my family and see mom. The upcoming days ahead were full of questions to the doctors as we awaited mom's results from all of the numerous tests the hospital took. On Monday, August 10, I was getting ready to run an errand for my grandmother as I stayed in Queens. But I stopped in my tracks when I heard the phone ring. Mom was on the other end and shared the grim news, "Serena I can't breathe easily because the doctor found large masses in my ovaries and tumors in my stomach."

I hesitated before speaking, "Mommy surely it's fibroids or they are benign. There's no way its cancer right?"

In a calm voice my mother replied, "The tumors are malignant. The fluid from my tumors reached to my lungs which is why I couldn't breathe easily. They plan on extracting the stuff out of my lungs tonight. I just need you to come."

"I'm on my way Mommy."

Before I hung up the phone, she said, "Don't tell Nana yet, just come so we can talk."

Obeying her demand I walked down the hallway and told Nana, "I'm going to visit mom for a bit to see how's she's doing." Looking back I think Nana knew something. There was an unusual nervousness in her voice when she asked, "Is everything okay? Can she come home yet?"

Not wanting my grandmother to know the full weight of the situation, I looked her in the eye and said, "I'm going to see and will let you know."

I jumped into a cab and went to Jamaica Hospital which was ten minutes away. I imagined the room to be dark and filled with demons meeting me at the door. When I walked into the room, I saw my mother resting peacefully. I kissed her on the cheek and she woke up smiling. The next few hours we talked about life. She held my hand and gave me firm instructions on her final arrangements. Towards the end of the conversation, I said, "Ma, we're going to beat this! I need you to believe me. Why do we have to talk about this?"

She smiled and said, "Serena, I'm so thankful and I wanted you to know that. Because, if I die, I don't want anything to be left unsaid."

Puzzled I said, "Come again?"

Mom said, "I'm so grateful. I have you, Christina, family and friends. I'm glad I had a chance to adopt Ayana and care for her before she died two years ago."

Here my mother was sick with the most advanced stage of cancer and she could still say how grateful she was. That night she taught me something in that dank hospital room. No matter how bad the situation seems or how deep the waters are, I should open up my mouth and say, "Lord, I Thank You for what I have."

I remember talking to God that night saying, "This isn't part of the plan." Mom and I had plans to hang out together and for her to see her unborn grandchildren grow before her eyes. She had already started preparing for her and my sister, Christina's future move to Alexandria, Virginia. Although Christina was nineteen years old at the time, she's severely autistic and couldn't live by herself.

We talked for almost a year prior to my move back east about what we would do. Mom even knew what type of place she wanted. She was getting papers in order in regards to my sister and she even bought household items for her new place. The news about my mother's cancer was naturally unsettling and all I could do was pray and asked God for strength as we set upon a journey we didn't want to take.

Almost every weekend, I either drove to New York with my friend Renee or caught a bus to be by my mother's side. Even when I got a job offer I asked mom, "What do I do? I'm so scared and maybe I need to move to New York and get something here."

She told me, "Don't be scared. Take the job, it will all work out. Plus, your spirit doesn't belong in New York. Please don't move on my account."

Mom was still parenting from her sick bed and I listened because she was right. Although I love New York I've always loved the DC area and wanted very much to live there.

At this point I would have given up my happiness just to tend to her care every day. But even though she was suffering with cancer she wanted me to be happy. She comforted me with her love. She also brought joy to the rest of our family, friends, doctors, nurses and even the cleaning staff as they were blessed to enter her hospital room.

My faith in Christ grew over the course of the next six months. I listened to Him more. Even when He said, "Stay home and rest." I was now a more firm believer and He was my doctor, healer, and financial counselor. God made a way for me to get back and forth to see mom on my limited income.

On Halloween weekend, I went to the hospital with Nana and the doctors pulled us outside of mom's room. I told them my mother had to listen as well because even though she had "chemo" brain from her first treatment she could still comprehend everything that was being said. "Chemo brain" is an unfortunate side effect where people become forgetful, repeat things, can't retain information the way they used too and even hallucinate.

We were impressed by the team of doctors that piled into the room who all saw to it that my mother had the best care. Mom smiled and greeted each of them. I couldn't believe her spirit as it shined through the whole time when the doctors told her it's either chemo therapy or nothing. Her cancer was inoperable because her lungs had been compromised from more of the cancerous fluid that was expunged from her tumors and now blood clots had formed in her legs. If they performed the surgery which would be a complete hysterectomy it would have killed her. It wouldn't have taken care of the stomach cancer and possible other areas that may have been effected.

I was on the verge of breaking down and as I hunched over the chair next to her bed I felt a force sit me back up. It was as if something pulled the back of my shirt and made me recline in the chair. I was at a loss for words but my mother began grilling the doctors with questions. Even my Nana jumped in and asked questions. By the end of the conversation mom said, "I'll continue the chemotherapy."

I walked into the hallway knowing that either the chemo would help or potentially kill her. A woman from the Palliative Care Team told me, "Just let your mother rest."

Scrunching up my face, I said, "What do you mean?"

The woman got closer to me and said, "Just let her go, Chemo will cause her more pain and may shorten her life. She's already weak."

I peered through the window of the hospital room and then turned back to the short and stocky woman and politely said, "Ma'am we've already prayed on it and His deed is done. Mom said she isn't going to die after this round of chemo. Don't you have faith?"

The woman stared into my eyes and said, "God bless you sister," and slipped away. I walked back into the room and sat with my mom for a little bit and then she turned to Nana and said, "You should go eat something Ma, it's been hours."

Nana chuckled and said, "Still giving orders from the bed Marguerite?" She slowly got up and left the room.

Mommy and I sat in silence for a little while, and then she finally turned to me and said, "Hold my hand please."

I held it and she said, "I feel comforted when you are here. I love you and I'm so thankful."

Trying to hold back the tears as my voice cracked I said, "I love you too, Bub and I'm thankful for being your daughter."

"Bub" was our pet name for each other. It came from a Tom and Jerry cartoon we watched when I was little and ever since we'd been calling each other "Bub." It still makes me smile.

Nana and I returned home in the early evening. My Aunt Hilda was at the house watching Christina. She explained to us that she had just gotten off the phone with Uncle Larry and he was on his way to the hospital. She thought I was going to head back to the hospital with her but I said, "I think you and Uncle Larry should spend time with Mom together as siblings before her chemo treatment."

Once Aunt Hilda left, I sat in the chair next to Mom's recliner and cried. It had been a long time since they all sat and talked as siblings. All the grudges and bad feelings were finally melting away. Aunt Hilda told me later that they were able to laugh together again, talk about the days when they all got in trouble and prayed with mom.

As the hours rolled by I called the hospital in the middle of the night to see how mom was holding up with her chemo treatment. She had received the first dosage and they gave her a break before she started the second drug. In the morning, one of the nurses called me and said, "Your mother is resting and took it well."

I bent over and the tears poured out. I said, "Lord, I thank you for keeping my mother. Thank you, God."

Everyday, mom had visitors; Aunt Hilda was at her side 5-6 times a week, Uncle Larry visited on Friday and Saturdays and told her stories about her ever busy nephews. Her best friend Kim, my cousin, Fern, who has the work schedule of ten people also visited regularly. Nana brought Christina to the hospital on Friday's with Uncle Larry. Christina would always lay her head on Mom's chest. One time Christina pointed out the chest port that was surgically imbedded into mom's chest for easy access to drawing blood and administering her chemo treatments. Mommy told her, "It's so I can feel better."

Every day I noticed a shift in my family. Mommy reunited us and we were on one accord again. Even my cousin Wayne visited. He told us he was supposed to go out of town and wanted to see mom before he left.

The doctor at Highland Care Center nursing home/rehab where mom spent weeks recuperating, was happy with her progress. He said, "I'm not God, I can't tell you how she's improving but she's holding on. Her CA-125 has even dropped."

Her CA-125 which is a protein that is a so-called tumor marker or biomarker went from three thousand when she was first diagnosed to seven hundred after her first chemo treatment to a whopping five hundred and eighty-five after the second. She still had a ways to go as a normal level is around thirty-five. The doctors were amazed she was able to walk when she was first admitted to the hospital with that high of a marker reading. He gave us that news on January 14th; two days shy of my thirty-fifth birthday.

Mom was blessed to have doctors that would defer to God when they couldn't explain things. The week after my birthday I made it to New York despite the snow that was still left over from the blizzard. I was recovering from a bad sinus infection. I didn't expect anything from mom. Just her presence was the greatest birthday gift I could receive. She and my Aunt Hilda had a birthday card for me and they were arguing over who should sign it. I finally said, "Mom please sign it, I think you can do it."

Although it took her a while with her hand shaking, mommy signed my birthday card. I held the card close to me and to this day it's on my nightstand. The next day we had a conversation and she started it out by saying, "I wanted to say thank you."

I turned to her and held her hand, "Ma, why do you have to thank me? This is what daughters do...right?"

She said, "I wanted to thank you for allowing me to adopt Ayana and Christina. I know it wasn't always fair to you because they had a lot of medical complications and took up a lot of my time."

My mother still had her memory, vision, although was blurry, and she even had her wit, but most importantly...she had her faith. I finally cried in front of her. I had wept before but this time the tears came out of me like storms on a gloomy day. I said, "Thank you for being such a remarkable mother. You raised me on your own and because of you, I'm strong and I love you for everything you instilled in me, the girls and the family."

We sat together for the rest of the day laughing, crying, and talking about how she missed watching her favorite pastor Joel Osteen and eating one of her favorite treats, "Junior Mints."

Every Wednesday when I went to my church Bible study, I thanked God for all He had done. Although I couldn't understand why Mom was sick, I always asked for healing for her body and I still thanked Him for the spiritual foundation that was holding us up. His undying love was reflected in my mother.

The call came at 4:40 p.m. on Thursday, February 18th. The doctors from Jamaica Hospital said, "Your mother's kidneys are failing."

I said, "I thought she was getting better. Her CA-125 was dropping and that's a good sign right?"

The doctor said, "Cancer sometimes hides itself in other places. The cancer is all over her body, Serena. You have to get here. She may not make it through the night."

Immediately getting off the phone, I called my Aunt Hilda. She was on her way to the hospital and said she would call me as soon as she got there so I could talk to mom. I drove to Alexandria from DC with tear-filled blurred eyes. It wasn't safe but I had to get home and pack.

I then called my friend Jeanette to tell her what was happening. Her only words to me was, "I'll meet you at your apartment, I'm on my way and I'll help you get home to New York."

After we hung up I then called my friend, Renee and she asked me, "How was I planning to get to New York?" My mind was in a fog and I couldn't think, after hesitation she said, "I'll put you on an Amtrak train and will call you later with the details of your trip."

Thankful that I had a friend coming over to be with me and the other working on my trip; I was now waiting on my Aunt Hilda and that was the longest 30 minutes of my life.

Finally I got the call from my aunt and she put mom on the phone. Her voice was strong through the speaker which made me smile a bit. I told mom, "I'm coming to New York and I need you to hold on for me okay?"

She said with strength, "Okay I'm holding and I love you."

Once I got home Jeanette helped me pack my bag and gave me a hundred dollars. Once I closed my suitcase our friends Candy and Joy called. They lost their mother to colon cancer in October 2006. I had always admired their strength during that time. I was sure they would share words of encouragement. But instead they told me something that I didn't want to face. Candy said, "There came a time when mommy was so sick and I didn't want to let go; but I knew I had too. I couldn't watch her being so sick anymore. Once you get there, if something happens, tell her, 'you can go' let her go and be with God."

Candy started sobbing, that's when I realized that the pain of losing someone you love remains very fresh. Frightened, I understood every word of what she said. I knew that mom's time was coming and she would soon be with God. I would have to grapple with helping her to let go. Candy and Joy's endearing words abide with me until this day.

I got to New York City at 4:00 a.m. on February 19, 2010 after fighting with Amtrak when the train broke down twice. Later in the afternoon, I sat with my mom and she asked me, "How bad is it Serena?" Pouring her a cup of water, I told her, "Ma, it doesn't look good..." my voice faded.

My mom didn't have much time left, so I wanted to hear her voice from that point until... I asked her questions about life, if I made her proud, any regrets and what she thought I should be doing? I promised her that Christina would be taken care of because the family would pull together to make sure she has everything she needs. With a sigh of relief she told me how proud she was of me and to not have regrets after I shared with her that I didn't even have any children yet. She smiled slightly and said, "I'll see my grandchildren soon."

We talked about our journey, her days of African dancing, adopting the girls, flipping through my baby book asking her why did she make me where an ugly coat. Oh, that got a good laugh out of her. Then she got serious and told me it's time to birth my dreams and it was time for my books to be published. She also talked about how God would deliver a good man to me.

I made promises to her to remain an advocate as I had been for several years after losing my grandfather to lymphoma and prostate cancer and keep running marathons on behalf of cancer. She instructed that I had to run in the full marathon (26.2 miles) that I had been training for through Team in Training the following month and to go to my friend's Adolphus and Monica's wedding which was the week prior to the marathon. I couldn't understand the instructions at first. I told her I had packed enough clothes to stay in New York for a while and wasn't worried about anything else. She then told me she was thirsty for something else besides water and right at that point my best friend Venetta and her father Sam texted me stating they were downstairs in the lobby. I knew it was prayer time as Sam always carried his Bible. I told her I'd be back and would bring her something to drink. We said "I love you" to each other and I left the room.

After greeting them I stayed in the lobby to call family and friends that wanted updates. I also took time to rest my weary eyes. After an hour Venetta and Sam came back downstairs and gave me their passes and said that they had prayed with mom and now she was resting. Right at that moment my cousin Fern walked through the front doors of the hospital. She had brought snacks for mom and I, since she knew that I hadn't eaten. She even brought something cold for mom to drink as her appetite was gone. When I returned at 7:20pm with my cousin Fern I noticed mom's breathing was labored and she wasn't responsive. I asked the nurse, "WHAT'S HAPPENING!"

He said, "I just spoke to her a minute ago and when I asked her if she was okay she said, 'I'm fine, thank you.'"

Then he turned to me and said, "Serena start talking to her, she's leaving us."

I stared into Fern's eyes briefly and then we both began rubbing mom's arms. I quietly prayed and then I laid my head on her shoulder. I was able to say in true faith, "Mom, we'll be okay, you can let go now…we're going to be okay, it's alright to go home and be with God."

Then I sat down and coupled her hands with mine and prayed like I never had before. I knew God and mom could hear me as I felt the force to keep the faith and to pray. I sensed that she wasn't just listening but she was holding me up. Her spirit was so strong that it helped mine during my weakest moment as she was already with the Holy One and our ancestors. We talked and prayed to her and at 7:42 p.m. she took her last breath. Mom believed that when she passed away she would die in peace. Although my heart is broken and I'm healing, somehow I'm able to stand, walk and smile about good times and memories. God has covered my whole family and friends as I watched my eighty-six year old grandmother send her third child home to God; she still has strength in her body to go on every day. Christina can still smile as we all can. Mom's siblings talk to each other more often. Faith kept us, His grace and mercy will get us through day by day.

Because of my faith in the Word I'm able to wake up every morning, pray, meditate, and talk to mom and other ancestors through prayer. I have peace of mind, knowing that she's with God and no longer in pain. *I listened*...something I don't do enough of. If I hadn't listened to God, I wouldn't have been able to spend all of those moments with my mother. My friend Jeanette and I sat on my couch five months after mom died and reflected on life. When she told me, "God was setting you up then for now. He used an old relationship to get you back into His arms again in 2004 and to create a spiritual foundation. He was setting you up for losing your mother."

In the beginning of the story you saw "Sauti" in my mother's name. That's her African name in Swahili given to her in the late 60's in her liberation movement days. All of the members of the International Afrikan American Ballet also called her by this name as well.

It means *"Voice."* Isn't that something? Her voice carried me and brought my family back together and even from heaven I feel her presence and love.

Lord, I Say Thank You! In my heart, mind, spirit and soul; I heard You, obeyed and listened to Your voice.

As we say in African tradition, Ase (pronounced Ah-shay) Mama Sauti for all that you gave me and us...Ase, Ase, Ase. "Ase means to give praise to those that have gone on before us...our ancestors." This story is dedicated to my mother, the late Marguerite "Sauti" Wills, May 20, 1949-February 19, 2010. May you African dance in the heavens and shower down blessings on your beloved family; we love and miss you.

Serena T. Wills a native New Yorker currently resides in Alexandria, Virginia and holds degrees from Syracuse University and Virginia Tech. Publication credentials include being published in a variety of anthologies and her first poetry book titled, *"Pieces of Life Volume 1, Reconstruction"* available at http://divinewryte.blogspot.com

God's Purpose In Our Pain
Angelia Moore

*A*untie! Something is wrong with Mammaw... she is acting funny."

"What do you mean?" I asked.

"She is not talking right."

"Let me speak to her... Mommy? What's wrong?

Mommy repeated what I said..."Wrong, wrong, wrong"

"Is it the baby?" She was babysitting like she normally did.

She responded... "Baby, Baby, Baby"

Something was wrong. I could feel it. My fear was that my mom had suffered a stroke. I called my sister and nieces... within ten minutes two of them were on the scene, one took the kids, the other called 911 and got Mommy to the hospital. I met them at the ER.

Both my mother and father have had near death illnesses more than once that called for extended recovery. So as bad as this was, it seemed normal, if there was such a thing.

We sat in the ER and waited on the verdict. We didn't call our father who was at dialysis; we didn't want to upset him. Some time later the doctor came in and told us that her blood sugar was low. We were relieved, but then he stated the other tests that were run had him a bit concerned and he wanted her to stay for a few days for observation. I called my husband and my sister. We figured out how we would rotate the time at the hospital. Mommy had started to come around, She was not as delirious as she had been upon arrival.

Two weeks later she was still in the hospital. Dr. Schaeffer believed there was something (a spot or mass) on her liver and he wanted to do a biopsy. But she couldn't lay flat for the duration of the examination. He stated that he did not believe it was as critical as getting to the bottom of why she was incoherent. He called in oncology, endocrinology, cardiology, and several other specialties. Now, our Faith in God was strong and we knew we were blessed to have physicians that were doing all that they could. Each day she was there, Dr. Schaeffer gave me or my sister a full report. He had spoken to each of the physicians and they collectively stated that it was okay to look at repairing her hernia, which she has had for a long time. They would identify the spot on her liver later when she was stronger. We were willing to follow any recommendations they had. Dr. Schaffer believed that my mother might have had sarcoidosis; a disease in which lumps of fibrous tissue and collections of cells granulomas appear on the skin and internal organs. He was very confident that this was the problem with her liver. Mommy started to improve. She remembered who we all were. She began asking what happened, her color was coming back, and she asked our daughter to bring her a Fill-It-In puzzle book. We were so relieved, because this is what we were used to seeing and what we loved about her. She asked the younger kids about school and their new teachers, etc. She states she was hungry; another wonderful sign as she had not eaten in several days. Dr. Schaeffer released her to a rehab facility and said she should be up and going soon.

After about two months in rehab, things were progressing well. We made sure one of us, my sister, Beverli, or I looked in on her daily. We brought our children at least one day a week. Now, she was not just the typical mother, grandmother or great-grandmother. Mommy had raised her children, actively assisted with all sixteen of her grandchildren and assisted or supported the raising of her cousins. That did not include the number of family and friends who stayed with us until they got on their feet. She never, and I do mean never allowed us to treat each other differently. She required us to care for and support each other. She instilled in us the true meaning of family... Family was not just those who are related by blood, but more importantly those related by love. Once we were considered family nothing could break that bond.

We anticipated her joining us for our biggest holiday dinner, Thanksgiving. However, things didn't go as planned. She was not able to make it due to a transportation problem. We were all devastated. It was nearing Christmas and she wanted us to go shopping for the kids and the staff at the rehab facility. We got the trinkets and things she request.

On January 24, 2010, I went for a quick visit to the rehab center to check on Mommy. She was in good spirits and we watched football and discussed if the Colts would make the Super Bowl. I contributed her good mood to the recent news that she would be going home on Friday. We were all excited. It had been a long six months. Then all of a sudden, Mommy looked like she had gotten overly excited. I said, "Calm down, what's wrong?" She said she couldn't breathe. I called for the nurse and she asked her the same question. The nurse listened to her lungs and checked her blood pressure. She asked her to calm down and said she would be back shortly. It seemed to get a little better, but when the nurse came back she took mommy's blood pressure again it was still not where she wanted it. The nurse told me she thought she should go to the hospital. My heart sank... things had been going so well. I began to pray and contacted my brother, husband and sisters. We all got to the hospital and Mommy appeared to us to be stable. Things seemed to calm down and Mommy was herself, checking on others, reminding us what we should or should not be doing. On Thursday, the rapid breathing increased again and I got the call that she was being taken to Cardiac Critical Care. That knocked the wind out of me. Now we knew it was pretty serious because there were several doctors, cardiology, critical medicine, endocrinology, surgery, etc in and out of the room. Dr. Roberts who was in charge of her care on this unit was just as compassionate and attentive to us as Dr. Schaeffer had been. That put our hearts at ease. We really didn't have anything solid on what was causing all of her breathing distress. But she was sitting up and talking, which we took as a good sign.

She still had those episodes of not being able to breath without extreme effort. Dr. Roberts told us he wanted to put her on a bi-pap machine; the machine eased her effort to breathe. Mommy didn't want it. She wasn't going to do it and didn't care what Dr. Roberts or anyone else had to say. So, my sister and I went in and talked to her and explained it was only for a short period to get her through some testing. She was reluctant but complied with our wishes. We decided to contact all our siblings and have them and their children come to visit and lift her spirits. So, on Saturday, January 30, 2010, the kids came. The hospital staff allowed us to close the door and we all reminisced and fellowshipped. The room was full of laughter and "don't bring that up." Mommy was doing so well; she had spent several hours with her grandchildren and great grandchildren. Beverli and I decided to go home and try to rest, since we had been staying at the hospital with Mommy each night.

Early Sunday around 5:30 a.m., I got a call from the nurse that Mommy was restless and she had asked for me and Beverli. I asked the nurse did anything happen over night because she was doing so well last evening. I couldn't understand why she was struggling and restless; since she had such a good time last night. She stated nothing really happened, but Mommy woke up and was

145

restless. The nurse had given her something to calm her a little and she was dozing now. I called my sister to tell her what the nurse said and we decided we would go straight to the hospital after church. But we could not really worship at church, because we were worried about Mommy, so we left and went to the hospital. We'd had enough experience with her being ill to understand, that if she wanted us there we really needed to get there.

We arrived and she was having difficulty breathing, again. However, we could see the relief on her face when we walked through the door. We tried to ask her what happened, why was she so excited? She kept saying she was tired. We contacted our siblings and gave them the update. The doctor came in and said he needed to intubate her to assist with her breathing again. By this time our brother and two of our nieces were there. Mommy was telling us; she was not concerned with what Dr. Roberts said, she was not putting that tube back in, at all. My sister and oldest niece tried to convince her it was best. She said, "NO," and "get out of this room." So, I went in and tired to talk to her. She told me "no." She then said that she loved us and we had been wonderful children to her. I explained to her this was just to help her breathe, nothing permanent. She said, "Whatever". I love you. I told her I loved her too. She very reluctantly agreed to be intubated again. The staff asked us to leave the room while they did the procedure. She had experienced intubation several times and it normally takes about twenty to thirty minutes. We called our father and gave him the update. He asked, "Why is she going back on life support? She doesn't want to do that." My sister and I tried to reassure him it was just until they can control her breathing. Our church family had arrived to support us. Our ministers, elders, friends and family were all there to help us through the struggle. We were surprised when it had been over an hour and no one had come to get us to go back in the room.

Finally, about an hour and a half later we are allowed in. She was resting and we were talking quietly in her room. Now, my cousin, sister and I were still there and I began to doze off. Beverli tapped me and said, "Look" at that very moment mommy's heart stopped. I heard the staff call a "code blue" to her room. I began to beg God for her and her recovery. The staff moved so fast I can't really remember what happened. I was holding her hand then I felt someone tapping me. I refused to move... I was in prayer and I was not leaving her side. I turned around and the unit secretary (thank God she was one of my sisters' in Christ) gently, but firmly told me, "They need room to take care of her." So I left and stood outside her room. I wasn't afraid or angry, I simply wasn't anything. Right then, I felt... empty... as if I had no feelings. Mommy had been sick so many times and had fully recovered, that I simply knew this would be another miracle. They were working hard in the room; it was like an episode of ER. Tears were running down my face and I looked at my sister and the sadness and fear she displayed hurt me more than my own pain. I wanted to comfort her but I couldn't – I didn't know how. I heard the chaplain who came because of the code blue, but I had no idea what he said. I did tell him we have our own spiritual advisors, but if he would like to pray, he could.

The next seventy-two hours were horrible. Mommy was on an experimental cold treatment. It lowered her body temperature to keep the brain damage to a minimal. Monday afternoon, Dr. Schaeffer came by... we went to see what he had to say. He began by saying, he was sorry she was so sick and he wished that he could do more. We looked up to make eye contact and he had tears in his eyes. We both began to shed tears with him. We completed the seventy-two hour process and they had begun to warm her up. The goal was once her body was back to 98.6, they would reduce her sedation and she would begin to respond. We watched anxiously as the nurse reduced the medicine and tried to shake her and move her. Nothing happened, so I tried, Beverli tried... The doctor came in and asked us what we wanted to do. He explained to us what had just happened. We decided to continue the life support until we speak with our siblings and dad. We had not had Daddy at the hospital a lot because he was not in the best of health and he went to dialysis three days a week.

The doctors did not believe there was anything else they could do. The hernia Mommy had for so long had become entrapped and was spilling toxins in her blood stream. She was too sick to even think about surgery. However, the doctors were limited in what could do. They suggested that we allow her to leave peacefully; Beverli was not ready to stop treatment. I prayed again, I called my godmother, my sisters in Christ to pray and our ministers, to pray with and for us as we made this decision. Dr. Wack, an infection disease physician, came in and discussed with all of us what was happening. Although it was simple to repair, the hernia had released so many toxins in her blood that to continue life support would only prolong the inevitable. Beverli understood and stated she didn't want to see her suffer anymore. We (my brother, Beverli, our nieces, my husband and her closest friends, and I) stood next to her as she slipped peacefully away to be with God. Nothing in my life could prepare me for the emptiness I felt when my mother left me in this cold, cruel world. Beverli went to tell Daddy.

Daddy simply did not know what to do, he could not believe it. "No, no, that's my Boo." He said. Our parents were married for forty-one years.

Now when Daddy told us he was done with this, we just thought it was his grief speaking. He had been sick off and on for the last four years. Our oldest sister was staying with him; Daddy didn't want to take his medication or eat. We rotated going to visit with him. On Monday, March 1, 2010, Beverli received a phone from the dialysis center. They said Daddy didn't come in for his treatment. We both called the house to find out he decided he didn't want to go. He had never wanted to do dialysis but went faithfully. We went to him. He said he was tired, and he was really upset that we were there. I brought soup and peaches, his favorite. We tried to feed him, but he refused and simply would not cooperate. We put Ensure in the freezer for later. Beverli and I explained to Daddy if he didn't eat he would need to go to the hospital to get fluids.

Tuesday morning I went to work, Beverli and our husbands went to see Daddy. The plan was if he was better we would get him to the doctor. If not; they would bring him to the ER. He was not doing any better and they prepared to get him ready to go to the ER. But he was not having it. He refused to get up, to help with dressing himself, etc. They got him dressed and had to physically carry him to the car. When they arrived at the hospital, he would not go in. My husband and brother-in-law got a wheel chair, picked him up and placed him in the chair. Now Daddy was a proud man; so when he got into the hospital he was talking, answering questions and being his quick witted self. The nurse told Beverli that he needed a CT scan and that he would be back in the area in about an hour. I arranged to leave work and met them in the cafeteria. We were down there about thirty minutes and began to head back to the ER when my cell phone rang. It was someone from the hospital. I answered and the nurse told me she was so sorry for calling, but Mr. Echols coded on the way to the scan. I couldn't remember if I responded or not. I heard her tell me he was in the cath lab and that we should get there right away.

We rushed to the lab and saw the same chaplain. My heart sank, the tears started to fall and I needed to sit down. Beverli simply said, "This can't be real." We immediately got our phones out and called our siblings. We worked in auto drive. Neither of us had really processed what just happened. We just waited to see our father and figure out what happened.

The chaplain went to get the doctor. The doctor came and told us that he had a lot of blockage and some serious damage to his heart. He stated he was not sure how things would turn out. They were getting him cleaned up and would have him in a room shortly. By this time, our brother, Isaiah, II, had arrived. The three of us stood with the doctor. I don't know about them, but for me it was almost an out of body experience. When he told us they were taking him to the exact same floor we had been on with our mother just about a month ago all I could think was "wow". The doctor explained the experimental cold treatment they would be using for him. It was the same thing they used on Mommy. When he was finally settled into his room we were told we could come and visit with him. We stood there speaking to him and each other and the patient representative from the hospital touched my arm. She looked at me and said, "Oh my God, I cannot believe you all are going through this again. If there is anything I can do to help you, please ask. My prayers are with all of you." I was humbled that she noticed we had just been there; yet I gained strength in her comforting words.

The next three days were a blur. Friday evening we were there and the nurse turned the sedation down and Daddy opened his eyes and looked at us. Our cousin was speaking to him and then he looked at the machines, the dialysis machine, the ventilator, the IV pole, the medications, heart monitor, and we could see the distress in his eyes. He looked back at us and then the monitor started beeping. The nurse said that he was getting agitated and decided it would be best to put the sedation back on. So we allowed him to get some rest.

On Saturday I asked the nurse how he was doing, she responded, "he's not doing well; you should call everyone." I was there at that moment by myself. I was overcome with grief, fear, disbelieve and any other emotion opposite of faith. I knew he was very ill, but surely God would not take my mother and my father in the same year! I went to the corner of the room to pray and to cry out to God, I needed something. As I began to call upon my Savior, I heard the nurse speaking to someone. When I finished my prayer, I was greeted by one of our ministers. I collapsed in his comfort and he prayed with me. I know God sent him to comfort me until my siblings could get there. He prayed, laughed and guided me through that rough time.

We all stayed through the night. At around 5:30 a.m., the nurse explained that he was really struggling and if we wanted to spend anytime with him we might want to come into the room then. I went and shared the information with my siblings who were bedded out in the waiting area. We talked amongst ourselves; Beverli and I decided to let our siblings make the decision of how to proceed. We came to the conclusion that we wanted him to go in peace. We told the nurse to make him comfortable. We spent the next three hours with him. He passed away shortly after eight on Sunday morning.

Now, I will not lie, I was hurt and felt so alone. Our family is very close, but there was nothing that could comfort me. I wasn't screaming and yelling. I was more hurting and distant. I know without a doubt that God doesn't make mistakes and that He had a wonderful plan for me. But I could not wrap my mind around how loosing both my mother and father was part of that plan.

Eight months later, and the grieving still happens, but I now see it as my own personal victory. My parents are resting; they instilled in us everything we need to meet them again. So, my focus now is doing all I need to do to get as many people as I can to join them.

Our lives will never be the same; we are experiencing all of the "firsts" (holidays, birthdays, etc.) without them. We support each other, encourage others and stand, knowing God is in control. Even when it seems that nothing makes sense, He has a plan to use us and all that we experience for His glory.

Rest in Peace, Mommy and Daddy, Rest in Peace!

Angelia L Moore, and her husband reside in Indianapolis, IN. They are the proud parents of 4 wonderful children. Knowing that God is faithful has gotten me through many trial and tribulations. I count my family (immediate and extend) as part of the rock that sustains me. Thanks to God for all He has done.
Contact Angelia at: email: anjeemoore@yahoo.com

Restoration
Minister Kim Jackson

$\mathcal{D}$avid the son of Jesse and Nehemiah were both builders of God's Kingdom and called to conduct war in their respective places. David was the warrior – a man after God's own heart. Nehemiah was a multi-tasker known for building while yielding his sword. I too have been called as a warrior and builder, in constant warfare to build retention walls for many while they mature spiritually, and then learn how to maintain their spiritual agility while on the battle field for the Lord. I have personally encountered situations while fighting for others that depleted my spiritual reserves leaving me urgently in need of restoration. What was the cause of the need for urgent replenishment? Had I not put on the full armor of God? (Ephesians 6:11)

On the battle field for the Lord I found that some of the very same people I believed to be on my side were in fact fighting against me. So I admonish you to watch as well as pray. (Matthew 26:41) Some of the battles I encountered were on jobs with supervisors, at home with family members and in the church with the saints of God. Truth be told, there are some battles that many of the saints of God endure that are in our mind as our spirit fights against the flesh and our flesh fights against the spirit. (Galatians 5:17) Once I stepped upon the battle field I could not decide to take off my gloves and retreat. Every warrior for God goes through training for encounters with the enemy. I got my warfare training while on the battle field and that's where God tested me to see if I was really "Keeping the Faith," regardless of the challenge He placed before me. Just know that He has chosen you to keep the faith for a time such as this.

Have you ever felt like you have walked in the shoes of Nehemiah the Warrior and Kingdom Builder, and then landed in the footsteps of David the Worshipper - a Man after God's own Heart? Perhaps you have been fighting your adversaries while attempting to build God's Kingdom, only for you to realize later that you have to flee from the very same people you aligned yourself with to establish the Kingdom of God. You may have felt like giving up even though you know God has created you to do greater works? Interestingly enough, though you were called to do greater works, you may have felt like you no longer had anything left to give. Some of the readers of this story may have even experienced a season or seasons where there were people, places and things that were unlawfully taken from you in the natural and/or in the spirit realm. Perhaps you've seen how people and things were deliberately separated from you and it is your earnest desire to have these things and people restored by any means necessary. If this describes where you are today, just know that God has promised you restoration. God has promised restoration for the assignments wherein you were called to spiritually impart into other followers of Christ. He has also promised restoration for the spiritual warfare that we - His followers have encountered in His Name. And most assuredly, He has promised in His word, "I will restore to you the years that the swarming locust has eaten, the crawling locust, and the chewing locust, My great army which I sent among you. You shall eat in plenty and be satisfied, And praise the name of the Lord your God, Who has dealt wondrously with you; And My people shall never be put to shame, Joel 2:25-27 (NKJV). This is the word of God for everyone that is keeping the faith. As I began examining this particular season of my life it was evident that I endured many battles and received numerous victories only because I am aligned with God to receive Jesus' restoration. If you are aligned with God and ready to receive your restoration – and you are fully persuaded to keep the faith – pray that your ears be attuned to hear what the Spirit says to the church, Rev. 3:22. Hallelujah!

When God restores His people He leaves nothing broken and nothing missing. I know for myself that God has the ability to provide restitution, rejuvenation, revival, regeneration, repair, renewal, resurrection, resuscitation and reinstate circumstances, people and things back to their rightful place that far exceeds man's natural ability (my own ability) to comprehend. There are several stories throughout the bible that tell of God's power of restoration. However no story told can be greater than the one's told of God's restorative powers accept those revealed by His courageous children who continue "Keeping the Faith." For it is within this great cloud of witnesses (Hebrews 12:1) that God reveals the manifestation of His grace and love, and we His people ultimately receive His bountiful blessings. When God restores His children we can't help but tell of His mercies that He allows us to see every morning. By telling our stories of faith, we encourage others to keep their faith in God. The Bible tells us that we should help restore our brothers and sisters in spirit of gentleness (Galatians 6:1). As you read my story you will see that this is the assignment that God has given me for you. Be excited to know that God is calling upon you and has the foreknowledge that you too will complete the assignment of helping others to be restored by your testimony.

Trials and tests surround every Christian. But what God wants to know is do we trust Him to be Lord? I have seen God perform miracles when there was no evidence of Him coming through, but I had to trust Him and not doubt. When my house was being foreclosed upon I had to surrender my abilities for His. I had

155

to pray and believe that God was the source of my supply because there was no other source. God sent a classmate to help me with the remaining amount within twenty minutes of when the payment was due. After rushing to the bank on a Sunday to make the deposit into my account and calling the company to let them know that the total amount was available in my account, I found out that the company was not on Eastern Standard Time. They were actually on the Central Time zone which gave me the opportunity for the payment to be received on time. Glory to God. His timing is perfect. God restored my ability to retain the house He had given to me and continue to pay the mortgage monthly on time from that point forward. I believed this happened because I faithfully relinquished me and sought God. Every day I see God restoring blessings that I thought were lost and I praise Him even more.

While reading Joel 2:25-27 I found God speaking through the prophet to the people of Judah to encourage them not to give up hope, but to Keep their Faith in God. He makes His intentions known through his written word that is indicative of His power to do all things. Joel admonished God's people to turn aside from their selfish ambitions and compulsions, for the ways of the Lord. By doing so the army that was sent by God against His rebellious people would be turned away and God would restore order to every facet of the lives of His people for the duration of the time of their original act of rebellion.

While writing this story I must say that God allowed me to see my previous sinful nature, how I was corrupted by sin and the purpose and process of being restored. Through it all He showed me that His loving kindness is better than life (Psalm 63:3). More than ever before I can appreciate this scripture because it reveals that because of His love, "He is faithful and just to forgive us of our sin and to cleanse us from all unrighteousness (1 John 1:9). I thank God for never turning His back on me and most of all for allowing me to be restored back to Him when I wanted to give up and to give in. Through several experiences I have come to know that it is during our least loveable times that God loves us even the more. Now when I recant being rebellious against God I grieve within and also remember the army that God sent against me. Know that when we come against God we will always lose.

I remember committing an act of rebellion against the Lord involving answering the call to ministry, because of the commitment and accountability required of me from the Lord. My story was just like Jonah's. Even in my delay I was taken through the refiner's fire. The purpose of the flame had not yet been revealed to me. But all the while what I did know was that it was for His Glory. The pain I endured while being processed under the flame made me feel like God was not watching over the temperature of the flame. In deciding to flee from the flames, I later found that I had only delayed God's ability to perfect me for the work that was yet to come. And yes, I had to go through some seasons over and over until the refiners fire burned off the excess within me that couldn't be used for ministry. I had to learn to quickly respond to God when He calls and when things get rough hold on to God, keep the faith, and trust Him to know that He watches over me even in the fire.

God showed me that He was a loving God and He has spoken, "For I the Lord thy God am a Jealous God.(Exodus 20:5) In as much as He loves us with an everlasting love (Jeremiah 31:3), because of this same love He has also allowed situations to occur to help develop my character and faith in Him. Don't think for a moment that God didn't see my acts of disobedience and that there aren't repercussions for disobedience.

157

However, my prayer for you today is that the sincere love that you have for God, be shown to Him by your obedience unto His directions for who shall separate you from the love of God. (Romans 8:35).

Some of the experiences I encountered that left me needing to be restored came as a result of my disobedience, at other times, situations occurred at the hand of other people's inconsiderate ways and in some other instances because of the divine plan of God. When I was disobedient, God showed me His jealous side so that I could see that He yet still desired for me to be restored back into a relationship with Him to receive His blessings, mercy and grace.

When God restored me unto Himself He enabled me to be whole, fruitful, properly positioned for Kingdom work, enabling life to flourish within me. I experienced several situations that required only God's restorative power. In this place of emptiness I needed Him desperately.

The Bible tells us to let a man examine himself.(1 Corinthians 11:28) In doing so I recognized that there was something going on within me that could be best described as spiritual depletion caused by spiritual fatigue. At first I couldn't identify with what was going on through my natural eyes. But through the help of the Holy Spirit I found out what precipitated my coming to this place. There were several answers including having a full-time ministry schedule befitting of one who does not have a full time secular job. However, I do have a full time job and I was trying to balance both. The next answer was being in constant spiritual warfare for me, my family and other saints of God, and it appeared that the enemy of my soul was relentless. I've never seen any fight that was pretty or fair. Life is not fair and neither is spiritual warfare. God would not have us to be unaware of Satan's tricks, devices or schemes in spiritual warfare. I didn't think that I was ready for spiritual warfare but when the fight was on and I was tested I found out that the gifts that were placed within me to fight were revealed especially when I needed then the most, that is when I asked God. Every act of spiritual warfare sharpened my skills and helped me to be fit for the next fight, which was always coming just around the corner. Strangely enough in between the fights I should have sought God to restore me but I didn't.

Though God's word declares that He would not have us to be unaware, especially when it comes to spiritual warfare, my encounters of warfare continued to be at greater levels and in a variety of situations. I encountered warfare to reveal the depth of my dependency upon God, what lied within my heart and to reveal the Spiritual fight within me. I fought in the spirit to have the abundant life God promised, to have His peace and to remain sane when I saw others being victimized. Spiritual warfare will either make you or brake you. My initial encounter in warfare left me licking my wounds but with every encounter I got stronger as the fight got harder. Some fights revealed situations that I chose to partake in and God didn't want me to.

In one instance God revealed that I participated in ministry assignments that God had not assigned to me and/or that I didn't take heed when I knew the ministry assignment was over. Interestingly enough I chose to stay with ministries way after my assigned time with them was over. I would soon come to regret this. Again-yes, there are ramifications for our actions of disobedience. But know that for those who are "Keeping the Faith," to obey is greater than sacrifice. (1 Samuel 15:22). By over committing myself I didn't give the proper time to the people and ministry assignments that God had assigned to me. Several times I didn't prioritize things correctly. I tried to do more than what my

159

creator had created me to do and I burned myself out. Even with all of my errors and mistakes God still loved me. And yet for a time I still hadn't learned the lesson to follow His ways which were greater than my ways. This inevitably left me open for another attack by the enemy and empty yet again.

In retrospect I am eternally grateful for the leading of the Holy Spirit and His revelation behind a strong feeling of unrest within me. In fact the Holy Spirit was unveiling what had contributed to this feeling of unrest, which was spiritual emptiness due to spiritual fatigue. I began to see things that were missing. No they were not misplaced nor unintentionally lost. I sought God to find out more about this specific area of spiritual emptiness, where I could go to retrieve the things that were missing and how to get them returned. Items were abruptly taken, removed un-seemingly, and/or disappeared subtly under questionable circumstances. I had experienced an unlawful theft in the spiritual realm. Within I carried a burden to repossess things that were stolen from me. I wanted them back and because I was determined to believe that I couldn't afford to lose anything else that God had given to me. Through prayer, lining up with the will of God, reading and speaking the word of God over my life and anything I was involved with, I began to see God sovereignly move and return that which was stolen. There were tangible items that were stolen from me including items from my car, jewelry, money that had been saved that continually kept being taken away. Then there were the intangible items that seemingly could not be replaced like time away from family to make money to keep food on the table, relationships with close family members, joy, and peace. I saw the act of having these things stolen from me as tactical maneuvers to distract me and to keep me from being focused on the things of God.

I marveled at how God moved and continued to move to restore the things that were stolen. Restoration of these stolen items and others that were listed wasn't instant but it did happen over time. Though things were stolen from me, God had a plan for me to receive blessings He had given to me to be restored. Not only did God allow me to see them restored but He magnified the unveiling of His power just so I could shout Glory. But I Had to Keep the Faith as I waited for things to be returned in God's appointed time. Therefore I continued to keep my Faith in God for therein lies the remedy for my restoration.

During one season I sought full-time employment for what seemed like an eternity to take care of the basic needs of my family. In previous employment I was unfairly treated, laid off, had employment contracts cancelled while working on-site at the job. I had the skills, experience and aptitude and often cried out where are you Lord and why would you choose me Lord to "walk by faith?" God showed me at a later time that He was a rewarder of them that diligently seek Him."(Hebrews 11:6) Because of the many unsuccessful attempts to gain employment I developed low self-esteem and fell into a depression. But God had another plan. With my back against the wall and me about to pull my hair out, God gave me the strength to apply for a job. The moment the documents left my hands I heard the Holy Spirit say, "I just wanted you to apply." The job I received from the Lord was made to order just for me. Not only does this job have me using skills that were developed while unemployed for several years, but my job involves working with Faith Based Organizations. God has placed me in a position to get blessed and to be a blessing. This job was surely a blessing from the Lord. Praise His Name.

Demands of Ministry

God says in His word "for my yolk is easy and His burden is light. (Matthew 11:30). In other words the assignment and the vessel assigned to perform the work on His behalf are to be a good fit. But He never said the work would be easy. Knowing this God admonishes every follower of Christ to be mindful of Keeping the Faith in Him, and to always remember "that it is He who has made us and not we ourselves (Psalm 100:3). We are called, created and purposed to Glorify Him.

I want to make it clear that being a servant of God (Minister of the Gospel of Jesus Christ) is not glamorous work, though some may have given it that impression. Ministry is a hard, self-less job that you must be anointed - that is empowered by God to do. Often many believers in Christ have counted the cost (Luke 14:28) to serve nations of people in a leadership role to impart hope and life through the word and power of the only true and living God. There is an unquantifiable amount of dedication required to minister, that only those who are chosen and answer the call to minister can perform through the help of the good Lord and by Keeping the Faith. This type of strength I am speaking of has helped me to stand my ground when I wanted to give up, while fighting, building, worshipping, seeking God's face and seeking Restoration. This strength sustained me when I encountered situations that made me question my faith and question the reality of the one who was, who is and who is yet to come, Jesus my Lord. Situations arose in this Christian journey that have brought me to my knees and in retrospect closer to God. So many times I could not believe the fight that was required of me to maintain my sanity as well as the mind of Christ, to maintain an attitude of contentment, continue to be obedient to God's Word while solely relying on God's will, and persevere while Keeping the Faith. But saints know that all the while many temptations of the world were calling me to revert back to its old standards and surrender to its strongholds. But the spirit of the Lord within me said no and took full dominion over my life. I've seen what I couldn't imagine, experienced things I had dared not to speak of, and ran from the very elect I thought were to lead me. I have been among brothers and sisters of Christ seeking the love of God and yet among them never finding His warm embrace. In one particular church I'm not able to recall hearing anyone teach of the work of the Holy Spirit. In another situation have seen Christians disrespect Pastors and try to take over their Pastor's leadership role because the Pastor's vision was not the same as theirs. Additionally, I have seen disorder in the structure of God's church and the misapplication of His word even though I know that my God is a God of order.

Though these and other situations that occurred left me wounded, the wounds were never too deep for God to outstretch His hand and perform surgery in areas that have impacted me, including the areas I don't want others to know about or at the time acknowledge. Our God is the Lord that healeth thee. (Exodus 15:26) in areas that you never thought would be committed by a fellow believer to you. It is important that I be real here because I know of many people in ministry that wear a mask to cover the pain and they never receive God's healing because they never ask God to heal them and wind up carrying their pain for a lifetime. There are some who never surrender the pain to Him even though God's word tells us to cast all of your cares upon me for I care for you. I admonish you my brothers and sisters to deal with the cause and effect of what has taken place that has hurt you. If not you may find yourself being a dead man walking. I used to be one. I was told by many to shrug off the situations that hurt me and toughen up. Over time I shrugged off the situations, toughened up and walls were built up. Because I did not give the situations to

God immediately and lay aside the weight that had so easily beset me Hebrews 12:1. I carried baggage that hindered my spiritual growth that got in the way of me receiving and grasping hold of deliverance from God. As I learned to take everything to God in prayer, the pain that transpired before I called upon the name of the Lord to heal me at times seemed unbearable. I have learned to quickly ask God to remove the hurt, help me to deal with the situation and forgive my oppressors. There is no way that healing could ever begin or be complete without me keeping the faith in the one who can do all things but fail for, "He restoreth my soul." Psalm 23:3.

If I had not dealt with the circumstances surrounding my pain, they would have continually dealt with me. Saints be confident in knowing that Jesus died for your restoration and He received stripes for the wounds His followers received while working on the front line just like Nehemiah and David. God is a healer. He died so that you can proclaim and receive your victory and restoration.

Several seasons occurred that left me desperately needing to be restored by God. I realized I needed to be spiritually restored but I had no idea to what degree. Surely we are surrounded by a great cloud of witnesses ((Hebrews12:1)) that will helps us along the way, along with the army of God united to protect and restore His children. I praise God that He used many Intercessors to pray for my Restoration.

I am so grateful for the many saints of God who have stood in the gap for me, prayed and tarried until my faith was restored. One of God's unique gifts to the body of Christ are His intercessors. Some intercessors were directly assigned to me that I know. Some others have come to know me just through seeing my face in the Spirit and they in turned cried out to God on my behalf because I had come to a place where I was so depleted that I couldn't pray for myself. Thank you Jesus for hearing "the prayers of the righteous that availeth much," (James 5:16) for my restoration.

My spiritual restoration was not an ordinary act and it required an extraordinary God, my God, "The Lord that made Heaven and Earth."(Psalm 146:6) He reminded me on several occasions that He makes streams in the dessert and rivers in the wilderness (Isaiah 35:6) Glory to His Name. In order for my restoration to take place I had to first acknowledge my need for restoration that only God could fulfill. Slowly I began to realize that the origin of my thirst was so much greater than my initial comprehension. No one ever said being a minister for the Lord would be easy. Look at what Jesus our Lord and Savior endured. He who was without sin took on sin. Jesus was used, abused and often ridiculed, as many of us His New Testament disciples have come to encounter including me. I have encountered leaders in the Kingdom of God that could not embrace, nor had any idea how to help in the development of the spiritual gifts given to me by God. Some others refused to acknowledge my spiritual gifts and there were others that saw the many gifts within me and chose to misuse them. In all of this I continued to pour unceasingly into the lives of many of the people of God with words of courage, hope and strength in Jesus' Name. But I soon learned that because I was not called to be all things to all men I had to slow down or run the risk of depleting the Spiritual reserves within me permanently.

When I am thirsty I can drink water, juice or even milk. But none of these liquids could give me the nutrients necessary to bring me back to that place of spiritual fulfillment and restore my passion for ministry. In order for the spiritual fulfillment to be performed I had to surrender covering up the many places of affliction, hurt and pain caused by not listening to God. Had I listened to God I would have known when enough was enough, be able to see when my gifts were perverted and in some circumstances where my gifts were only tolerated. The spiritual outpouring into God's people at times was monumental. God showed me the need for balance, a lesson learned.

God's plan

Every move of God is designed to draw us closer to Him and to take us closer to our destiny. God has told us in His word in Jeremiah 29:11, "For I know the plans that I have for you declares the Lord, plans to prosper and not to harm, to give you a future and a hope. Because I know God's word is true, I found myself asking the question again why me. Why had God chosen a girl who grew up poor (though I didn't know it until I was grown), in a single parent household (my father died at the age of twelve), who became a mother of two children (yet was never married), excellent career path in public health and education (though always the one to be laid off instead of others though my skills and background were diverse, having a quiet temperament (yet speaks boldly through the fire of the Holy Spirit), called a social butterfly according to my mother while growing up (to later be set aside to walk an often lonely journey), and who's life seemingly has been a constant challenge to become who I have been called to be in God's Kingdom. All of these things happened amidst a life often times filled with distractions and totally dependent upon God. This was not my plan but I believe it was God's plan to allow me to go through and He would show me the way out, so that I would bear witness to His Glory and be restored.

God is strategic in everything that He does. His supernatural abilities cannot be patterned, but can only have the believer awestruck at His timing, and ability to see, know and do all things but fail. Often I looked at my situations with the why questions. Only to later see why in one circumstance it was necessary for me to go in to the bank at almost closing to give my testimony to the clerk of how God supplies all of my needs according to His riches in Glory, (scripture) for the mortgage payment that was put together to keep my house from going into foreclosure. What an incredible God He is. I was chosen to share my story with the teller about my full trust in God, for a time that was yet to come, to reveal that I truly was "Keeping the Faith."

I came to know that every battle God would fight. But saints have you ever thought about what happens when your muscles are sore from swinging the sword of the Spirit or when your breast plate of righteousness received a dent in the middle. Perhaps your helmet of salvation didn't have a good fit and even came off during a fight leaving your mind exposed and you questioning your relationship with Jesus. Has there been an instance when you know that you have girded your waist with the belt of truth, though you continue to be tempted to believe that your belt of truth is getting loosened by the negative words of other believers speaking over your life. You may find yourself in a position where your feet hurt just for making a stand of faith even though you know that your feet have been shod with the preparation of the Gospel of truth. And now here you are left you with no desire to take another step and the impending day foretold of the wicked one is here. Have these situations arose and you have found yourself bent over from multiple warfare encounters or are you standing firm holding up your shield of faith and trusting in the Lord our God the entire way. If this is you and you have been seeking an answer to why, just know that God has chosen you to endure on His behalf and He will restore you to your original position in the Kingdom regardless of the experience on the battle field and the state of your armor. You may have questioned how many more circumstances will He call you to, why must you have mangled armor and how much more must you endure in the name of the Lord? He has shown me that I am capable of handling more than my mind can conceptualize. But when I have endured like a good soldier He will restore the protective gear necessary to cover me to be used for another day and another battle if I would just continue "Keeping the Faith."

I believe in God's word that declares "to much is given much is required." God has purposely given me a variety of situations where He has tested my faith for Him to restore me and allow me to write my personal reflections of these situations, along with His revelation for my Victory. Additionally, I also learned to own my personal responsibility for being depleted and needing urgent restoration, to "forgive them for they know not what they do,"(Luke 23:34) and to "forget those things which are behind and reach forward to which lies ahead, (Philippians 3:14) " There is absolutely no way for me to believe in the God of my Salvation while going on these walks of faith without keeping the faith, for my Restoration.

Though I know that I have been called to speak life to many nations, I first had to be restored by Jesus. While in a worship service the Lord began to speak to me about Restoration. If I earnestly surrender my life unto Him, He would Restore the gifts that had laid dormant, my heart from being broken and disappointed, my desire to pray and intercede though often times I ran away, to be purposefully placed in His Kingdom so that I can come into the fullness of God, quench my hunger and thirst for righteousness, increasing my sensitivity for His Spirit, believing that He has given me dominion and authority for I am not defeated, and enable me to be cleansed from all unrighteousness.

I am now able to walk in my season of victory, restoration and refreshing because I have surrendered to the hands of the Potter to be reshaped, yet again. It is my prayer that you receive restoration in every area of your life when you surrender and continue Keeping the Faith.

Minister Kim Y. Jackson, M. Divinity is the President of God's Glory Publishing. She is a sought after conference speaker, workshop facilitator and teacher. As a scribe for the Lord she details the plan of God for His people. Minister Kim Y. Jackson has written several self-published books including "In the Garden" - a woman's journey orchestrated by God for deliverance and spiritual maturity."

To contact Kim, please visit: www.kimyjackson.org or email her at: writethevizn@aol.com

Not Left Behind By Faith
Nicole Smoot-Miller

$\mathcal{M}$y father, James E. Smoot, was a devoted man of God. After serving over twenty-five years in the United States Air Force and retiring, he became a member of Mt. Pisgah Baptist Church where he grew older, wiser and became a dedicated servant. He volunteered to drive the church bus and became the grounds keeper. It wasn't long before the church realized that he had a heavenly voice and he joined numerous church choirs, where he used his God given gift to sing sweet melodies. He also was a member of the usher board, a Missionary Chaplain, and a Layman. He also served diligently as a Deacon.

Years later he began suffering from arthritis, high blood pressure and major knee problems (resulting from years of military service, playing sports and basic wear and tear). Eventually, he had to have his left leg amputated. However, he was still able to drive himself around and tend to his missionary work with even greater determination. He continued to serve God – by attending church regularly and continued to serve on several organizations at the church. Dear to his heart was visiting the sick and shut-in, praying with them and also delivering communion to them. Not only was he a man of God, but he was also an excellent family man. He was a devoted husband and a loving father and grandfather. If anyone needed anything, he would stop whatever he was doing to satisfy their needs. Many sought him as a mentor and confidant. Because of his testimony, many came and gave their lives to Christ. He was a humble servant, short on cash, but overflowing with love. His favorite scripture was Acts 3:6, "Silver and Gold have I none; but such as I have, I give thee: In the name of Jesus Christ." There were often times when he may not have felt like attending church services; however, you could always count on seeing him on the front pew with the other Deacons leading a song, reading a scripture, or praying. People would always say to him, "Smoot, I don't know how you keep going. Do you ever slow down?" His response would be, "I've got to serve God and do for others while I can!"

When his time was drawing near, it seemed as though he knew that he was going home to be with God. He had planned *and* paid for his own funeral services, which included picking out his own casket. He also had on file at the church his own funeral services typed out, including who was to sing, what songs he wanted sung and who was to do his Eulogy. I can recall having several conversations with him earlier during the month about older church members that were ill or in nursing homes. When I asked him how they were doing, his response was, "Sometimes they know you are there, sometimes they don't." Then he turned and looked at me with an expression I can't even begin to explain and said, "All of us old timers are getting out the way now." When he made that comment, I think my stomach literally dropped to the floor. He also began remodeling his home by purchasing new carpet and flat screen televisions for every room in the house. He continued to treat the wood on the patio, hung the enclosed patio cover, installed the hanging chandelier outside and made sure his surround sound was running smoothly. He told his wife, "When I'm gone from this earth...I want you to sit and enjoy these things, and remember the good times we've had." He also spent numerous days with his youngest grandson, who is ten years old. He was particularly excited for him, because he was scheduled to get baptized on the first Sunday in August. He wanted to prepare his grandson for that special day. He made sure he was at church every Sunday, gave him a Bible to take to

Church and helped him understand what being baptized and serving God meant. In addition, he was also planning a surprise birthday party and other family oriented fun-filled events for his sister, who lives in Richmond, VA. She was due to arrive on Wednesday, July 29 with her two children and two grandchildren. But that was not fast enough for dad, he kept calling them double-checking that they were still coming and encouraging them to come sooner. On the Monday before their scheduled arrival, my father and I talked as we normally would every night. However, the conversation we had was as if he was preparing me for his home going. He told me, "Regardless of what it takes, before I die, I want your sister here before the end of the summer. I have to tell her what I want done when I'm gone from this earth. She is the oldest and I want her to know what I want done when I die."

Again, my stomach felt like someone had just knocked the wind out of me. The only thing I could say was, "Okay dad, I love you and I will talk to you tomorrow." I had no idea that would be my last conversation I'd ever have with him.

On Tuesday, July 28, he was preparing for an evening church service for the Laymans at Zion Hill Missionary Baptist Church. Before leaving home, my step mother recalled that he looked really good. She joked with him saying, "Boy, are you sure you're going to church? You are looking too sharp?" Earlier in the year he purchased a beautiful dark suit with a matching tie that he had set aside and told my step mother, "This is the suit I want to be buried in. This is the one!" Coincidentally, that particular evening he decided to wear that exact suit to church. As he walked out the door, his wife gave him a kiss and told him she would see him later when he came back home.

At Zion Hill that evening, he gave an extraordinary testimony about his wife's medical test results, how good God had been to him and how he was so happy God had blessed him all these years. Then he sang, 'Amazing Grace,' like he had never sung before. He sang so well, that some people stood up, while others sat on the edge of their chairs. Then he said, "Church...I got to go! I'm getting out of here, I'm leaving this place," and then sat back down in his seat. He then set the microphone on the ground and quietly laid his head back and at the age of seventy-seven years young, went home to be with God. That particular day was cloudy outside; Therefore, there were several clouds located above the church. However, immediately the sun opened a large hole in the sky causing rays of sun to shoot through the stain glass windows of the church – as if my father's spirit and soul was being lifted up into Heaven.

The question is, "Does a person know when they are going to die and does God send them signs to get their house in order?" Since my father was extremely religious, I feel that he was very well connected to God who was telling him, "Servant, well done! Your job is complete. Your house is in order and now it's time for you to come home and be with me." My father would always say, "When I have sung my last song and prayed my last prayer, I'm going to give God all the praise, honor and glory!" And that is how he ended his life: Singing and giving God all the Glory before quietly leaving this place.

After my father first passed away, I began to think, "What am I going to do? I can't live without my dad. I want to leave this earth and join my father in heaven." That was until my son (my father's youngest grandson) looked at me and said, "Mom, stop crying. If you leave me, how do you think that would make me and your other children feel? We would be hurt and feel exactly how you feel. You know what you need to do? You need to pray.

Grandpa would tell you to leave it all in God's Hands. God will not put more on you than you can handle."

I looked at my son and knew that the time he had spent with his grandfather had paid off. His grandfather had taught him to be strong and how to lean on God. At that moment, I realized that the passing of my father meant it was time for me to get *my* house in order, pray and get a closer relationship with God. At first I did not understand death and was upset with God for taking my father from me. After having that discussion with my son, I realized that dad's passing was a true miracle. He was slowly preparing us for his departure. Now as we gather the puzzle pieces together that he left behind for us, we realize he was a walking angel on this earth. He was also a living example of how being handicapped does not have to slow a person down. As my father would say, "May the works I've done speak for me." I can truly say that the work he did on this earth is truly speaking for him. I know that he is in Heaven looking down on us. As we place the puzzle pieces together day by day, we now realize that we had an earthly angel that walked the face of the earth for seventy-seven years.

Two weeks before my father's death, I had a dream. In my dream, a lady dressed in all black including a black dress suit and black hat with black veal came to me and said, "How strong is your faith in God?" My response was, "I don't know." She said, "I want you to work for me." The next thing I knew, we were standing in a store and she asked me again, "How strong is your faith in God?" Again, my response to her was, "I don't know." So, she pulled out a black box and said, "Any questions you have....All the answers are in this box. Again, I'm going to ask you, how strong is your faith in God?" My response to her was still, "I don't know." Then she pulled out a business card holder and said, "Any questions you have, you can find the answers in this book." At that point I woke up from me dream.

When I woke from my dream, my first response was, "What is God trying to tell me?" I started going down my list of possibilities of things that could happen in my life that God could be trying to warn me about. I was thinking maybe my troubled son was going to get into something at school or in the streets. Then lastly, my thought was is something wrong with my parents or is something going to happen to them. But then I reassured myself, "No, everybody is okay - that was just a bad dream." The question that later came to mind after my father's death, "I wondered if God was trying to prepare me for my father's death through my dream." As I continued to go on day to day, I realized that the dream could have also been one of the puzzle pieces that was preparing me to accept what God was soon to bring to pass in my life.

After my father's death, I started second guessing my faith in God. I kept recalling the dream over and over again and kept having flash backs of the lady dressed in black repeatedly asking me, "How strong is your faith in God?" At that point, I had lost total faith in God. I had no desire to attend another church service, read the Bible or pray another prayer. I was so full of anger. I also became very distant from family and friends and could not focus at work. So, not only had I lost my father and lost faith in God, I was now on the road to losing the people who cared about me the most, as well as losing both my jobs. For the first few months, I don't think there was a single day that I did not go visit my father's grave during my lunch hour and cry like a newborn baby; not to mention there wasn't a single night which I did not cry myself to sleep. I was in a total state of depression. Finally, one day after going through a box of my father's items that my step mother had given me, I found a CD labeled 'Left Behind'. This CD was one of a series that Pastor Edwin K. Bryant (The same Pastor of our church who also did the eulogy at my father's funeral) preached about during the month of August. I thought, "Mmph! I had nothing else to do, so I decided to listen to the CD.

As I sat and listened to the sermon, I remembered being at church the Sunday when Pastor Bryant preached that sermon. I may have physically been present in the church that day; but, my mind was somewhere else. After replaying the sermon over and over again, I began to understand why God let me to listen to this sermon. Pastor had made me realize that the last thing I needed to do was forget about God. From that point on, I realized I needed to stay close to God, because He would work everything out.

There were several key factors in that particular sermon that shined light into my life. The first thing that caught my attention was when Pastor Bryant said it was okay to weep when a person feels they have been left behind; but that we should work while we weep. Therefore, it was time for me to start working for God in God's house. I needed to find an organization to join that would allow me the opportunity to reach out to others. As I continued to listen to the CD, Pastor Bryant also showed me that I needed to reorganize my plan as well as reconnect my purpose.

That day, my thoughts drifted back to May 2008 when I almost lost my life due to a major surgical error. I had promised my dad that if God would bring me out of this health crisis, I was going to give my life back to God and use my health experience to reach out to others.

After fighting for my life for nearly three months, God had answered my prayers and restored my health. I was able to return to work, as well as continue most of my normal activities. However, my father's death has been the real epiphany I needed to finally reconnect my purpose. I needed to find Jesus, reconnect with Him. Ask Him to help me through my problems and to give me the courage to PUSH through it! Matthew 6:33 says 'But seek ye first the kingdom of God, and his righteousness; all these things shall be added unto you.' As the elder members of the church would say, "Trouble doesn't last always!"

After listening to the CD, I started thinking, "Nic, look at you. What have you done to yourself? You know that your father would not allow you to get down like this." I began thinking about several things such as: when was the last time I went to church? Or spent time with my kids, who'd just lost their grandfather who had been the only father figure in their lives? In addition, when was the last time I prayed to God for health and strength and took time to read the Bible? The most important thought that kept popping in my head was what my son said to me when my father died, "Mom, stop crying... God will not put more on you than you can handle!" That has been my most inspirational reminder that started me on my way to begin a better relationship with my Lord and Savior.

The next Sunday, my family and I attended church. Followed by the next Sunday - to the point where attending church had become part of our regular routine, which was a major step for me. Don't get me wrong, we did attend church often prior to my father's death; however, now I began attending faithfully and paying more attention to the sermon. Years before, I always said that because the kids participate in sports, such as football, cheerleading and basketball, we couldn't attend church on Sundays. However, now that I have obtained a better relationship with God, I realize that if I am able to get up and go to work every morning and take my kids where they want to go, I need to show God that same respect and get up on Sundays to attend church. I had failed to remember that if it wasn't for God I would not be able to work or do the things I want to do.

Years prior before my father passed away, he would always arrive at church before us. So when my children and I got to church, it was habitual for us to begin looking for my father's head bopping on the front row. If I couldn't see him, I would just listen for his strong singing voice that often overpowered the choir. Because my father was a Deacon, I knew he would be somewhere on the front row of the church. So naturally, after his death, I had to re-adjust myself and stop looking for him at church. There were times when I would cry during service and run out of the church. However, the more I began to lean on God and continued to attend church, things in my life slowly began to get better. In addition to attending church, I also began reading the Bible. My favorite scripture that continues to give me strength and encouragement is Proverbs 3:5-6, "Trust in the Lord with all your heart and lean not on your understanding; in all your ways acknowledge Him, and He will make your paths straight."

Just as my faith in God was beginning to get stronger, I came across another bump in the road. I received news that my sister (my dad's oldest daughter from his first marriage) was diagnosed with breast cancer. Once again, I felt as if God was testing my faith. I began to think out loud, "God, why are you doing this to me? This has got to be a mistake!" Since my father's death, I now considered my sister the *Leader of the Pack*. I began to think, "God has already taken my father away from me. Was he now going to take my sister away from me too?" That is when I *really* learned how to pray on my own and learned just how powerful prayer can be. I remember falling to my knees and speaking to God as if he were sitting there with me, begging as if I was a little child or asking God for forgiveness. I was determined that I was

178

not going to allow the devil to win this battle; I wanted him to realize this battle belongs to God. I prayed and cried until I couldn't cry anymore. I asked God to heal my sister and give her the strength and energy to oversee this diagnosis. As my Pastor would say I had to PUSH (Pray until Something Happened). Shortly after receiving the news from my sister about her cancer, she had surgery a week or so later to remove the cancerous lumps from her breast. Test results later confirmed she was now cancer free, but she would still have to take medication for the next few months. Mark 11:24 says, "Therefore I tell you, whatever you ask in prayer, believe that you have received it, and it will be yours." This appears to be a true result of the saying, "When prayers go up...Blessings come down." I remember my father would use that saying various times throughout my life, not only as a child, but also when I became an adult. However, not until I felt like my life was coming to an end, did I really begin to understand what my father meant when he would use that saying. He would also say with a smile on his face, "Somebody prayed for me, so now I must pray for somebody else." I did exactly as my father told me, and I prayed for somebody else.

I have now regained my faith in God, learned to trust Him, and also learned to enjoy life after being left behind. I was once told by a good friend, "A person cannot enjoy life, if you don't know how to trust God." That same friend encouraged me to borrow her CD by Joyce Meyers entitled *The Cause and Cure for Worry*. The CD simply stated, "The cause for worry is... not trusting God, and the cure for worry is... trusting God."

There are still some days when I think about my father and find myself worrying about my life and I start to shed tears. But after I shed my tears, I feel refreshed and begin to PUSH until I get the results I am searching for. We as Christians, might not like or understand the things that God does, but God does things for a reason. One of the most inspirational lyrics ever sung states, "He's an on time God, yes He is." With that said, God has truly been there for me, and taught me to never lose faith in Him. As I sit back and remember the last weeks of my father's life here on earth and recall several of our conversations – God was working through my father to prepare us for his departure from this earth. It is now time for me to gather the puzzle pieces that were placed around me, begin picking up the pieces and putting the puzzle together.

It has been a little over a year since my father went to Heaven. However, now that I have gathered the puzzle pieces together, which included: praying and pushing, weeping while I work for God, re-organizing my plan and reconnecting my purpose through prayer; I am now ready to follow in my father's footsteps and serve God and do for others while I can. I can no longer cry and mourn his death - for he has gone to a better place. I now have to work towards making sure I reach those pearly gates of Heaven to reunite with my father. With God's grace, I can help others understand how to enjoy life and how to have faith and trust in God when they feel they have been left behind.

Nicole Smoot-Miller of Dayton, OH attends Sinclair Community College majoring in Business Management and Journalism. Her professional career specializes in Real Estate/Property Management as well as Customer Service. Nicole also attends Mt. Pisgah Missionary Baptist Church. She is a devoted mother to three beautiful children ages 18, 15 and 12. To contact Nicole email her at: nmillertyme@hotmail.com.

In loving memory of
James E. Smoot
January 8, 1932 – July 28, 2009

You have gone and left me behind, but in my soul you'll
always shine.
Even though you're not here, in my heart you're *always* near.
Rest in peace with God!
From your loving daughter,

Nicole

Waiting for Arella Noelani
Arnita Fields

So it came to pass in the process of time that Hannah conceived and bore a son, and called his name Samuel, saying, "Because I have asked for him from the Lord." 1 Samuel 1:20

God is a God of covenant, and He is faithful to what He has promised us. Over the years, I have found that during the times when I have humbled my heart and submitted my entire will and desire to do things according to His established plan; it blesses not only Him and me but others as well in the long run. When praying about what to write for this anthology, I heard immediately in my spirit that I must uncover and share the scars associated with waiting in faith for God to bless my husband and myself with children of our very own. Although we do share an eighteen year old daughter with her birth mother, our desire of having children together was something we had wanted since we met over thirteen years ago. When I went to discuss with my husband my new assignment (I always do this with any new writing project), I asked if he was comfortable with what I was released to share with my reading audience. He looked at me and said, "I'm good, I'm okay with it,". So with my husband's blessing and the leading of the Holy Spirit, I am completely free to share with you a testimony which is near and dear to my heart.

Over the years I have received many a puzzled look as I would talk with excitement and enthusiasm about the children that my husband and I would have some day. In addition to believing God for children I have even gone as far as to have picked out and have prayed over the names of each of my children for over the

182

last nine years. It was decided that if we were to have a son, that he would of course be named after my husband, and if we had a daughter, she would be named Arella (messenger) Noelani (a heavenly mist). Even to this very day when I lift up others for prayer, I make sure to lift up my unborn children and give thanks to God the Father for His established will coming to pass in their lives. Some of you reading this may assume that my desire for children may seem a little way out there, but to others who know from your own experiences that it takes consistent faith and obedience to move the hand of God especially when you know that what you believe God for can't happen without His intervention.

For many years I have walked in what some people call radical faith because I believe God can do anything, for real. I truly believe that there is nothing that my God can't do. I have personally seen God heal, restore, renew and revive dead situations and issues over the years not only in my own life but in the lives of so many countless others. There were some things that I thought I needed or wanted in my past that did not come to pass, but the desire for the deep down things that I knew God had placed in me have and are still coming to pass to this very day. The word of God tells us in Matthew 19:26 that all things are possible with God because all it takes is someone to stand and believe in God by faith. Now, let me share with you my journey of how I am still standing in faith as I am "Waiting on Arella Noelani."

Growing up as a child, my baby sister and I would spend a lot of time discussing the things we wanted to have as adults. I desired as many young girls had, to attend college, get married, buy a home with the big backyard and picket fence and then having lots of children. Looking back now, I know that God's word is true when it says that God's ways are higher than our ways. Although, I had planned out the order of how things should happen in my life, I even had the nerve to go as far as gathering specific details of what I wanted my future life to look like. Of course by now you may have gathered that things did not work out the way that I planned. God knew the plans He had for my life even before I was formed in my mother's womb. I had to learn that God's will always win out when it comes to my life.

Looking back to 1988, while dating a young man who will remain nameless, I had become pregnant. As a young child and then young adult I had always experienced some of the most unbalanced and often times frightful menstrual periods. When I say frightful, I went to bed some nights with so many layers on because I did not want to wake up with my mattress soaked in blood. You may be wondering what does this have to do with desiring children. Well, for me this issue marks the very point in time where my life was forever changed because my body rejected something that was so precious to me. I can still remember how cold my Ob-Gyn was the day I went into his office because I had been bleeding and clotting off and on for almost five months. This type of bleeding had happened before, but the length of my cycles had gotten longer and longer. After my examination my Ob-Gyn gave me a calendar and ovulation thermometer so that I could take my temperature daily and find out the time of the month I ovulated. I had no clue what he was talking about, because I didn't know that I had been pregnant. And I wouldn't even have a baby to show for it. I received a D & C, a thermometer and then the doctor sent me on my way. I must admit that right then I was hurt and mad all at the same time. I did not need a thermometer; what I needed was some grief counseling and therapy to get over what I had just been through. I got up from that narrow table, gathered my things and left his office never to return.

In March of 1998, six months after my wedding day my husband and I found ourselves sitting in the waiting room of my Ob-Gyn. When we were finally called backed to her office, we were handed the type of news that would devastate any couple and especially a young couple who were still newlyweds. The doctor told us that I needed a complete hysterectomy to alleviate the pain and stress I had been experiencing monthly. To this day I can still remember the look on my husband's face as we both turned to each other and froze. I remember turning back to look at my doctor and before I knew it out came a sound from way down deep in my belly. I screamed, "No." I then told my doctor that I would not have the surgery and no, I would not give up on the promise that I knew I had from God. It was then that my husband and I gathered our things and left the office and returned to our home.

That same evening I had many thoughts swirling through my mind, as my husband and I both tried to make light of the situation and not focus in on it too much. But later on that night as I lay beside my husband thinking of the fact that I may never be able to give him the children that we both desired; I then began to feel like an absolute failure. As I talked with God, I reminded him of my husband's son who had died of SIDS (crib death) only eight years prior to our marriage; and now we were being told that we wouldn't be having any children together, ever? To tell you the truth, it was during this time when my emotions really took a nose dive, both naturally and spiritually. In clinical terms it would be said that I had spiraled into a deep depression. First my husband's grandmother passed, then a few months later out of nowhere my maternal grandmother who I was really close to became ill and died days later in the hospital as I stood holding her hand. Right then it seemed as though I had entered into the deepest valley experience in my young married life.

Soon the thought of having children was no longer at the forefront of our minds because our hearts had begun to shift to the matter of trying to save our marriage. After only three years of marriage, my husband and I separated and went our separate ways, it was then that the dream of us having children died right along with our marriage.

During our separation, while living in Nashville, TN, I continued to make periodic Ob-Gyn appointments because I had to keep up to date on what was still going on in my body. Although I was celibate, I would still get up every morning and anoint my belly with blessed anointing oil and say that the fruit of my womb was blessed, in Jesus name, amen. As the days went by, I began to have more trouble as the fibroids grew larger on the inside of me. As I sat once again in one of those crazy half gowns on a bed small enough for a toddler, my Ob-Gyn came in to talk with me after she had completed a biopsy of my uterus. She then said to me, "I want you to try these pills and if they do not work for you, I'm sorry to say, but you must have surgery to get these fibroids removed." I told her okay, that yes I would take the pills, and yes, I would stop drinking coffee and cut out eating chocolate every day. I then asked the Lord to help me with the coffee and chocolate as I got dressed and headed home still cramping from the pain I experienced after the biopsy.

In 2001, I attended my former church's annual women's conference being held in a local area hotel. The conference was especially exciting for me because I was not on my monthly and I did not have to deal with any crazy pain or discomfort. The special guest speaker for one of the nights was Rev. Jacqueline McCullough, whom I was so excited about because she was one of my favorite speakers. Over the years I had followed her ministry and even had the opportunity to meet her in 1996 when she came to speak at my former church in Memphis. It was during this very special night that the process of healing began to take place in both my body and womb. During the service a strong healing anointing fell upon the place as women rushed the altar to be healed of what was ailing them. Finally I was able to make my way close to the altar, but as I got closer I went out like a light as Rev. McCullough stretched her hand out towards those gathered in my area. My faith had been ready for God to do the miraculous and now it was finally before me. As I came from under the power of God, I slowly opened my eyes to see the precious face of my pastor's wife along with one of the church elders who were both standing over me fanning and praying. As she laid her hands upon my belly I literally began to feel all warm and fuzzy inside. As I got up I realized that God had performed spiritual surgery on me. Later on that night, in the hotel room, my monthly came on completely unexpected; it was like someone had turned on a water faucet. Honestly, I got a bit upset because I knew that God had healed me and I was not excepting "no" as an answer.

That next afternoon, I received yet another word of prophecy concerning my giving birth to children. When I heard it, I pondered for a moment and then took it and placed it up on the shelf along with the other ones I had received concerning this very same thing from over the years. I knew that once I got home from the conference that God was going to deal with me one on one to help me with what I was really feeling deep down in my heart. Besides this, I was still standing in faith, believing God for the restoration of my marriage so I knew that something had to take place with that before the children would even come into play.

In 2003, my husband and I had began talking again; I was

excited about this because God was keeping His promise. We both had never wanted to divorce anyway; we had just allowed the cares of life to contaminate our faith. Although I was still living in Nashville, we would talk on the phone a lot. By this time, a lot of my menstrual pain had subsided and I was taking the pills which were prescribed to me two years prior. The purpose of the pills was to keep my cycle regular and to make them shorter. Although my cycle was still about ten days long, that was a whole lot better than going four weeks to two months long. When I did finally make it back to Memphis in 2004, my husband and I had fully reconciled and continued to work at getting back on the right track and the same page with each other. Although I did not bring up the fact that I still wanted us to have children, I quietly decided that it was best for us to just take things slow and only one day at a time.

Once our yearlong courtship was over and things had settled down by 2005, I made an appointment to see my new OB-Gyn. Because it was a group of physicians I was seen by the first available doctor who happened to be named, Dr. Lazarus. When I heard his name, my spirit leaped, as I let out a loud, "yes!" As my husband and I waited for him to come in and do the ultrasound, we once again began to talk among ourselves about the possibility of having children. When the doctor came in and began the ultra sound, I almost sat up in the bed as I watched the monitor. Is, it? No, it can't be. Yes, it was true. On the screen as he rubbed the instrument over my belly I did not see one thing, not one fibroid floating around in my belly. There were no fibroids! When the test was over, we met with Dr. Lazarus in his office. It was at that point that he confirmed that I did not have fibroids, but a condition called polycystic ovaries. I believe I went someplace like lala land because I really was not paying him any attention when I saw with my own eyes that I did not have fibroids. The tears had already begun to flow from my eyes down my face and onto my blouse. He then said to me, that I had apparently been misdiagnosed. I assured him that yes the fibroids had been there because I had seen them myself on every ultrasound for the past seven years. As Dr. Lazarus left the office, I looked at my husband who looked at me with a "for real" type of expression. I then wiped my tears and told him that I knew when God healed me; it was on that night at the women's conference back in 2002. Although it did not look, feel or even seem like I was healed, it was that very night that God had dried up those fibroids on the inside of me and allowed them to flow right out of my body! To this very day, I still praise Him about my miracle. I know for myself that He is a healer because He personally healed me, Glory Hallelujah!

Although my husband and I were still unable to conceive because of my polycystic ovaries, I still got up every day and anointed my stomach with oil, declaring that the fruit of my womb was blessed in Jesus name, amen. I believed with all of my heart and soul that my womb was still blessed and that one day, at God's appointed time I would have an opportunity to meet the son and the daughter that God has handpicked just for me. Even after all I had been through there was no way I was giving up hope of having my own children. God had given me a measure of faith and I kept my measure working night and day believing God to do the impossible.

The struggle was not over for me. In fact, in 2009, during a routine pap smear my Ob-Gyn noticed something wrong with the culture she took and asked me to let her do a biopsy right away. My faith could have fell flat on the floor right then but as I laid there waiting on her to return, God gave me peace and told me to go on and let her test a sample of my uterine lining. I complied and went home to tell my husband the news. As I watched for his expression, it seemed as if he was thinking quietly, "Can my wife even get a break from all of this?" That evening, we decided not to talk about it because God had given me peace about what was going on. I did not want to hear the negative opinions of people who did not understand what I was going through emotionally as well as physically and spiritually. During times of great testing and uncertainty, I had learned to protect my measure of faith from those whose measure was polluted with the mindsets of the world. After the two week waiting period passed, I was summoned to my Ob-Gyn's office. As she gave me my biopsy results stating that I did not have cancer, but she also gave me the news that I had to make a decision right then about having surgery within the next two weeks. She said that she could prescribe me some pills that would take probably a year to work or I could go ahead and have surgery. I had to pause and then say what? What surgery? She then explained to me that there was a huge cyst sitting in the wrong place and that it was better to have it removed before it caused any complications. As I sighed, I heard immediately in my spirit to go ahead and have the surgery, and that all would be well. I read over and signed the release papers to schedule my surgery later that next month before I left the office. While getting my blood pressure checked one of the nurses said to me, you are going to be just fine. And you know what, she was right I was going to be okay. As I walked down the street back to work I asked the Lord, what was all of this really about, like I didn't know already? I had never had surgery before other than the previous biopsies, so God was going to have to really help me with this thing about being put to sleep for sure.

Following a successful surgery, performed by none other than Dr. Lazarus (because my Ob-Gyn had to take off) I had the opportunity to be off from work for six weeks so that I could heal.

The time off proved not only beneficial for my body and soul, but for my spirit man as well. The surgery was successful and the follow up appointment showed that the cyst was indeed benign; I could not help but wonder, now that the surgery was over, what was the next step in this already long process leading up to us getting pregnant?

One would think that maybe I should just forget about the deep desire to have children and maybe become a foster parent or adopt some children, but it was hard for me to lay my Isaac upon the altar. Although some may think that because I experienced huge obstacles and challenges with my body over the years that this should serve as a large enough wake up call for me to realize that I am not supposed to have children of my very own, but there is still this thing about faith. Although my body has been telling me no for many years, my mind and my heart are still telling me yes. Yes, I will go forth despite the challenges I have faced. Yes, I will keep it moving and not let it bother me when people don't say Happy Mother's day to me even though, I am already the special mother of an eighteen year old daughter. No, I will not let it bother me anymore when people say, oh yeah; you don't have kids, so you don't understand. And no, I will no longer feel like a failure because I am not a mother yet. I am going to remain focused and keep moving forward, because God made me a promise a long time ago and, as Abraham did, I will hold onto my promise until God tells me otherwise. When He tells me something, I believe it and that settles it for me.

At this time, I would like to specifically speak directly to the women who are wives that may have suffered in their bodies as I have. If you have experienced crazy pain in your body, or have dealt with what seemed like endless cycles, or encountered some embarrassing near misses while at work, church or out in public, it's okay because you are not alone. You may have even cried puddles of tears in the midnight hour because you felt that no one understood what you were going through, it's okay because you were not alone. I'm here to tell you that God has not left you or forsaken you, He has been with you through it all. He knows what you are going through because He designed you according to His purpose. Your story, your testimony just like mine can help to set many women free from the bondage of hiding an issue just because it's embarrassing. I am a firm believer that God does not allow our life experiences to be for naught; but they are to be used as tools to help others see not only His mercy and grace but His unfailing love.

It has now taken twenty-three years for God to fully heal me of the pain associated with my miscarriage. As each year passed there was layer upon layer peeled away as my heart, body and mind were restored. Jesus came to heal me and I know that He is ready and willing to heal you too. Allow the love of God to come into your heart at this very moment to uproot the bitterness that has been sitting in your heart because of your barrenness. Your being barren does not mean that you are not loved. Hannah was barren and therefore, she is a perfect example of this very fact. She allowed herself to become extremely bitter because her husband's other wife provoked her to jealousy year after year. When Hannah's husband realized she was unhappy, he could not understand her grief because he had always poured out his love on her both naturally and materially. The depth of grief and pain in Hannah's heart, was the basis for her missing out on living her life to the fullest because she had allowed her barrenness to become a priority for many years.

Am I still waiting on Arella Noelani, my answer to you would be a definite yes. But while I'm waiting I am making sure that I do not miss out on the life that God has for me right now. I have a wonderful husband of thirteen years who loves me and makes me laugh daily. I have a special daughter who is a freshman in college. My parents are both prospering in life and doing well, and I have five of the best siblings in the whole wide world, along with twenty-one nephews and nieces and six great nephews and nieces. While I may not be a mother in the natural, I know that I am loved daily. Truly, I am a richly blessed woman who has a wonderful and incredible life ahead of me and for that alone, I am grateful.

So to my married sisters who are yet waiting to birth forth their very own Samuel; I say unto you, go in peace and live, enjoy and love now because you are already blessed and highly favored of the Lord.

For more information on finding a Gynecologist in your area, you may visit the website of the American College of Obstetricians and Gynecologists at www.acog.org. For information concerning the new HPV test, you can visit their site at HPVtest.com.

Arnita L. Fields, blessed with the opportunity to author four books of Christian poetry, award winning author and writer Arnita L. Fields is destined to make her mark in the literary arena. Arnita is a wife, special mom, minister and full time student completing degree work in the field of Counseling Psychology.

Unchartered Waters
Pam Osbey

Be strong and courageous. Do not be afraid or terrified because of them, for the Lord your God goes with you; He will never leave you nor forsake you. Deuteronomy 31:6.

Even though I sat in a dark room, scratching my head for solutions that would not come and wiping tears that fell from questioning eyes, I kept pace with the clicking of web pages searching for that extra something that could give me a little money on the side. Instead of going into my prayer box, I figured I would eventually come up with the solution to the problem myself. My mind was wracked with cloudiness as various bills stacked up on the corner of the desk hawking at me. Scattered papers lined my desk and the only light shining in my bedroom was from my personal computer. Maybe if I revised my resume, that would be the blessing I needed. Shoving that idea out of my mind, I minimized my word document, and let my finger stay still as I sat musing on my current dilemma.

Although my heart wasn't into the search for yet another job, I pushed on and continued looking to see if I could find another gig to give me financial cushion in between my main job as a literary teaching artist. Earlier in the week I had resisted God's advice, ignored the voice of reason, and signed the contract pushing ahead to work another year in a very challenging situation that would push me over the edge. The main issue I was dealing with had to do with the way I got paid as a literary teaching artist, which consisted of a five week timesheet that was not paid out until eight weeks later sometimes. This translated into me not getting money up to two months sometimes. In the meantime, I

194

had to rely on my other small gigs if they paid me on time. The life of a self employed literary teaching artist was a hustle that no one really understood except for me and those who actually lived this life.

I thought I was starving for my artistry, but what I was really doing was starving for God's guidance and love. Instead of allowing my flesh to call the shots, I should have been allowing the master to prune and order my steps. Following them would have been much better than avoiding the summons of eviction I'd just received. Last summer I searched for jobs aimlessly. I didn't have much to eat because I couldn't afford to live in my comfortable South Shore apartment. I was only half paying my rent, as I tried to keep my lights, cable, and internet service on. It was extremely hard to admit to myself that I had to make some changes and quick.

Shutting off my own thoughts, I heard the jingle of the phone and ignored it as a job posting in my Gmail account gained my attention. It was a rejection email by Teachers for America. I really wanted to teach full time, get certified, and get noticed again. Tears begged to stream down my stubborn cheeks but I silently wished them away, ignored that sting beneath my eyelids as I felt that lump in my throat. I pushed away from that awful pain.

Many emotions poured from my being as I stared at the screen, wishing the result could have been different. At that moment I felt worthless… like no one would ever hire me for a full-time position. Maybe it was the devil knocking on my shoulder mocking me, smothering negativity over my spirit. Suddenly a calm feeling washed over me as I scanned the website after reading the response from the embedded link. Apparently, Teachers for America, had an opt out list or you could be added to other job listings through them. With the spirit of curiosity coming over me, I decided to click 'yes' to adding myself to the database of non-profit job offerings, even though deep inside I felt I would not be exploring any of them. What was the use?

Although I didn't want to admit it, I hadn't asked God for His opinion on what I should do. Like most backsliders, I had felt that He wasn't going to answer my prayers in the time that I needed. So why should I get on my knees? Little did I know that knee mail is the best mail. I started packing up my apartment, room by room, after having called my brother and asked for advice. I came up with a plan and began my transition for my move. Serenity opened itself inside of my heart as I began cleansing my apartment of the old stuff I had allowed to stack up over seven years of living on Chicago's south side.

On the last day in the apartment, I had a talk with God. A long over due discussion about my life, what I had contributed to it in the madness of living on the lame for over a year and half, while pretending that I had everything under control. Shifting myself onto my knees for the first time in months, my brown eyes filled with wetness. Tears fell to the ground as I began to commune with my Lord. Words filled the room as my voice cracked with emotion and reverence.

"I know I don't deserve Your love or Your kindness. I shouldn't be asking for anything, Lord. But, like grandma used to say, *I need You to give me a word and Your grace.* I need something, from You right now, I know nothing. I am nothing. I am the vessel you created and I need you to take me to a place of humbleness I've never known. I need to shut up, and let you show out. From this point on, I am going to allow You to prune, mold me and make me Your humble servant, please Lord. In Jesus name, I pray, that whatever I say or do from now on, reflects You

196

in the best possible way. I need to remove me, and replace you on the inside and outside of me. I know I don't deserve the breath in my lungs, but if you order my steps, I will follow the path you create."

As the soft words bounced off the empty walls of my one bedroom apartment, I began heaving, allowing the stress of self inflicted pain to flow off my being, grasping the tattered pages of the Bible I had been studying since the age of eight. The same Bible that I received as a little girl from my mom. The same Bible that I carried with me through all of my days of living at home, to going to college, to moving from the south suburbs of Chicago to the south side.

God's word wasn't hidden from me, only I had stubbornly refuted it as if I had all the answers already and I didn't. Grasping onto the word this time would be my lifeline and I had to carry it with me. I wasn't sure where I was going to go after I moved out of the apartment, and part of my flesh was horribly embarrassed that I couldn't provide for myself anymore. One thing was certain though, and that was the love of God and His grace would carry me. Just how far, I would see in the coming year as time rolled on.

Spring 2009 found me finishing up my last year in the Chicago Public Schools, where I had been teaching poetry to grades K-12. After the eviction, my lovely mother gave me the chance to restore my spirit by living rent free in her empty home, in the south suburbs. I was really humbled and grateful to stay there. The past months had been the best ever in a wonderful journey where the father and I communed regularly. I spent a lot of time in prayer and in reflection. I felt more certain about the purpose in which I was fulfilling through my temple. Knowing that at the end of the day, I was going to be productive and stay focused on God's direction. God made me feel blessed in ways I could not explain to my friends or family. I didn't think there was a word or phrase that could capture the essence of my faith filled life. I felt happy but uncertain about my future but was hopeful things would even themselves out.

Then an odd situation occurred during my wonderful break from the schools that would change my entire world. I received an email from my employer about my poetry programs ending in four days – no prior warning, just a long email apologizing that the arts funding for the city of Chicago had been depleted. Due to the recession, we couldn't get any private funding either. All classes would have to end by Friday. I had been looking forward to planning the summer literary events at each of my schools. This was the best part of the programming, where I actually got a chance to coach students on performance and theatrical techniques to use on stage as young artists. Not to mention, the hard work we'd put into the anthology had now been ripped to shreds because they canceled that also.

I was in disbelief as I stared at the screen. I said a silent prayer and then called Cassie, my coordinator. Having been supervised by one of the best literary coordinators in my eight year stint as a literary teaching artist, was a bonus and I absolutely adored how she related to her team. She was always calm, even when things were going awry. She was so patient, kind and resourceful. I just assumed that my call to her would be resolved with a quick answer that would satisfy my needs.

"Hey Cassie, can you let me know if we really have less than a week to finish all programs?"

My voice was cracking as if I was ready to rip her head apart and that wasn't my intention.

Her soft voice flatly stated, "Unfortunately, funds have run out, Pam."

Sitting in the kitchen, I swung my legs and stood up with negative energy flowing through my entire being and began pacing the floor.

"So you're saying, that's it. We're done for the entire year?"

"Yeah, sorry, that's it, Pam. You can continue at the schools beyond that date, but they won't be able to pay you for your work. I know it's hard but the same thing is happening to me as well."

Stumped, I sat down, frowning, and twisting the cords of the phone in my jittery hands.

"Are you still there?"

Twirling a long dread lock in my finger, I absently answered, "Yeah, I'm here. Thanks for the clarification; I just wanted to make sure. I guess I'll see you when I pick up my last check or at the exit interview."

"That's true. Take care of yourself, Pam. You did a great job this year."

My heart fell, just thinking of how I was going to tell the students my time was over with them. I had spent the rest of that day talking with a few close friends and my mom about my predicament. Instead of getting upset or mad at the Lord, I just continued with my day. I felt that one door closing may be an opportunity for a blessing to come through and give me the push I needed to move out of Chicago.

Over the past year I had been talking about moving out of Chicago but I wasn't sure where I would go. Again, I had to really stand still and allow God to fill my being with patience so I would not make any missteps as I reached a decision. I kept myself open and kept the lines of communication flowing to God's hotline. Later in the week, I received a notice for several job opportunities through the Teacher for America list serve I had signed up for a few months prior. One job peeked my interest. It was in New York

City working with a non profit, doing youth development, which was my specialty outside of teaching literary workshops.

The job didn't pay much at all. So, I didn't tell many people that I applied for a job that would put me at the poverty line. Besides, I didn't even think I would get the position. I put it in the hands of God. I figured if it was meant to be, it would be. After all, he had given me faith to endure all the life changes of the past month, getting evicted, and allowing others to really help me as I readjusted to a new life. He had always provided for me from helping me to breath, to blocking negative energy from my life, to making sure I was on the right road to fulfill His will.

Worrying about whether or not I was going to get the position wasn't going to do anything but make my head hurt. So, I continued to strive for excellence that week, going into schools, smiling my way through lessons with my elementary and middle grade students, and treating all personnel with the upmost of respect. I was determined to let God's light shine as I walked the streets of Hyde Park, Englewood and West Pullman.

Day five of the week would find me totally immersed in faxing timesheets, and emailing reports to Cassie, and then breathing a sigh of relief that I had done what I was supposed to.

Like Ruth in the Bible, I had experienced really hard times, some of those times were self inflicted while others were lessons I had to experience to be molded in the image of what God needed. Ruth and I shared a lot of commonalities, she experienced economic hardship and so did I. We both had experienced loss of something we held dear to our hearts, and ended up surviving and thriving as a result of God's grace. Walking away from Chicago would be unexpected but just like Ruth I would have to lean not to my own understanding but allow God to navigate me into uncharted waters.

The weeks went by quickly, I spent a lot of time, resting and spending time with my inner circle. I was a home body; cooking fresh meals from scratch, and keeping my mom's house clean. I was in solitude for much of that time and ignored the devil's call to give in to any temptations of the flesh or other things that would take me off my path of peace and serenity. The simple things in my life helped me appreciate the blessings I had already been showered with.

God has promised that if I would be faithful to Him, He would do miraculous things in my life. That meant, I needed to stand still and obey his wishes. That meant saying no to my flesh, my personal wants and needs and to focus on what his will required me to do. During this time, I spent a lot of time realigning my connection to God, studying the Word, going to church and staying loyal to Him. Being faithful doesn't mean you just give up something because it's uncomfortable; it means you have to carry on straight through until the end. To unconditionally commit to following through on what you said you would.

The experiences of waiting allowed me to increase my personal communion time, delving deep into worship, praise and walking the walk. Confessing my personal sins and allowing God to re-order my steps so I could fully allow God to shine brightly in my life. I knew I wasn't perfect and would never be, but I knew if I stayed true to the word that I gave God he would make a way out of no way.

The beginning of a new life came in the form of an unexpected job offer from a government organization, (AmeriCorps) which selects community members to serve in different communities in underserved areas. The position that I was being offered was on the East Coast, in New York City. It was under the umbrella of a program being financed by President

Obama with specific funding from Washington, DC. I was joyful as the sun shined again on my soul, letting me feel its breeze of life and for a moment, I thought that it was a temporary solution for a longer problem. I figured I would work a year and then come back to Chicago. At least that was the plan.

My new position came with the lowest salary that I had ever had in my adult life, but since I was broke, and no Chicago positions were available, I chose to take a leap of faith into an unknown ocean of life. I packed my bags, left a place I had known since birth, for a city that had experienced its own rebirth after 9-11. Rebirth is a beautiful thing that if allowed, will branch itself all over you and create moments of growth that will empower you.

The moment I said yes, to the position, all kinds of doors opened in my life. Three of my closest friends, contacted me and put cash in my hand, took me shopping for clothes and out to dinner before I left. I was still humbled by it all but knew deep in my bones that God had given me all that I needed to start my new journey in NYC. With three hundred dollars in my pocket, a laptop and two suitcases, I raced through Chicago's O'Hare airport with a very good friend. I gave her a huge hug, and made my way, ignoring the fear that had embedded itself in my spirit previously. For there is no fear with God; there is faith, love and strength in His guidance. I knew He was in control and I had to relinquish it in order to grow and coast the new waters he had just placed me in.

As I settled in my seat at the plane, I felt the divine love wash over my spirit. Tears welled up in my eyes as I felt God's grace opening doors that would position me for an increase in my life. Not a financial increase, but an emotional and spiritual increase that would not only bless my life but others.

It's funny how God began ministering on my behalf shortly after I arrived in New York City. With the program funds not readily available, I ran out of money, two weeks after getting to New York City. On my last day in a hotel in Harlem, I had been tossing and turning, still trying to control my life and not allowing God to completely reign over it. Thus, when I ran out of money and waited for money to be transferred to my bank account from Chicago, I immediate told a few of my new colleagues about my circumstance. Everyone was pleasant and listened to me but that was it.

I was on my last day in the hotel with no back up plan of housing. Coupled with the fact that my family was in Chicago. I kept one thought going through my mind, "God is not fear."

I chanted it to myself, grinning like I'd won the lottery but it was just me pushing through my worries. As I sat in the crowded room, I had wondered where I was going to lay my head that night. After contacting a good friend online she had said she would check with her pastor to see if I could crash somewhere in the middle of the Bronx, but that never happened. So I was back to square one -- no solution and maybe that was the beauty of it all. So, I waited for the master to check His inbox and see my virtual message. I would have to allow it to stay with Him and let Him work it out. There was no sense in me trying to constantly micromanage the situation because he was the one who steered me in this place of newness. God could create a blessing like no other. I just had to believe.

Needless to say, the consistent phrase was running through my mind like a song. During training for my new position, one of my colleagues approached me with an idea about my living situation. She said she had talked with her husband and they felt strongly that God wanted them to open their home to me. A stranger! I started humming louder and louder as I walked away from her with praise pouring from my grateful mouth. I had only met Mandy once during the previous week and really didn't know much about her but I knew God. I knew that if God brought her to me then it was a good thing. He knows exactly what he is doing. I had to trust that and allow Him to provide for me in the way He saw fit.

Most people I knew would never stay with a stranger they had only recently met. If I had told my family that I was living with a stranger, oh boy! They would have thought I had lost my mind. Trusting God was the lesson here for me. I had always been a person who planned everything out. I never did anything spontaneous and I liked having that control. What God needed me to do was give Him the reigns… let Him guide me and trust Him completely. I had to live the life I sung, studied and cried about. Yes, I had to put this into practice, and be a light for the world around me to show others who didn't believe. I wanted everyone to know that He lives, He lives! How would I show my works if I didn't allow Him to use my life as an example of His grace?

Later that day, I ended up going home with Mandy and met her wonderful husband John, both faith-filled individuals who hadn't known me from a hole in the wall. Mandy was a fellow AmeriCorps member who also worked in the Bronx. Her husband was studying to be a minister. They resided in Yonkers, NY and just happened to have a spare room that I could sleep in. I still couldn't believe that I wasn't homeless after running out of money earlier that day.

I called my mom and told her the situation, she said, "God is going to bless those people, because they didn't have to do that!" I had to agree.

Not many people would open their doors for a stranger. But they had and I was grateful for it. For the next three weeks, while waiting for my paycheck to be cut, and money from a previous gig in Chicago to hit my account, I didn't have to worry about money to eat lunch or dinner because I was eating at Mandy and John's apartment.

Not only did God provide a roof over my head and food for my belly, I felt safe. The area was beautiful. It had man made water structures, a walking path, and most importantly, it was peaceful. I would hear the birds at night and cry into my pillow because of the love shown to me. I knew it was a gift that I could not take lightly.

Everyday was seen as a gift in my eyes. I had keys to the apartment, could get in and out when I needed to. I felt forever indebted to this couple due to the unconditional love they spread on my thirsty soul. They gave a stranger the ability to recharge her batteries and become centered. They also offered a place for me to lay my head without any expectations. It was quite an experience that I will never forget.

I began to feel as though I was God-employed and felt very encouraged by the fact that I was doing so much with so little. It was something that really made me rethink how the world influenced me in terms of focusing on material things, and discounting simplicity.

During my time with Mandy and John, I was able to really meditate on God's word and see blessings unfold. I was without my normal amount of clothes, but I still needed business attire. Mandy took me to a neighborhood clothing exchange. I grabbed a few shirts and skirts and felt so happy. A few of the items would serve as my business attire until I received my first check. After gathering items, I settled in for the night and thought again about how awesome my God is!

Thoughts like that danced around my head as I transitioned from Mandy's place to a condo God allowed me to live in shortly thereafter. I moved to Parkchester, which is located in the North East part of the Bronx. Living there was a test of my character and further molding of my spirit would occur. As months moved into a full year of being employed, I experienced several things that helped me to get closer to the throne.

God knew that moving me out of my comfort zone would cause me to have more focus and I would be tested by different people, experiences and the culture of New York City.

I prayed a lot, on the way to work, while at work, and read scriptures to give me spiritual food to think and live by. I began worshipping with a fellow co-worker who also was a transplant from Illinois and together we were able to share testimonies and trials. In terms of my walk with God, I began to separate from the world in regards to my thought processes and how I carried myself as a young lady. This included checking my online pages at Myspace, Facebook and Twitter, to make sure all my public imagery would be pleasing in God's sight. I didn't want to have any alluring pictures or even intonation of things I would say, to be not appropriate.

I then connected with an online group of spiritual sisters who were on fire for God. I began joining a few online communities that discussed a lot of issues dealing with living the life of a Christian single. This included opportunities to get support from other brothers and sisters in Christ. It helped me get closer to what I felt deep in my bones. It opened my heart further to allowing God to mold me into a deeper reflection of His love.

Challenges came my way through my new experiences, and every time, I'd send some knee mail to God, open my Bible to study or find a way to go into my prayer box to focus more deeply. My dedicated prayer time is one of the things that enabled me to keep God within the bosom of my heart, even on the lowest of days. This was the first time in my life that I allowed Him to stand front and center and not try to micromanage God's guidance in my life.

After my first year ended in New York, I was still working hard and wrapping up projects. My professional life was great but personally, I was still struggling financially. Piles of bills were stacked up in my file cabinet and I couldn't pay them at all. So, I continued praying for full employment by the end of the summer.

Two weeks before my volunteer position ended, my student loans unexpectedly went into default and as I sat at my desk contemplating what to do, God already had the answer. He had it covered and although I cried in the midnight hours, He hushed and held me. A few weeks later, all would be resolved and for that I am still grateful.

Other issues like living with three roommates began to grate on my nerves. Due to my volunteer status, in order to have housing, I had to get roommates. This really tested my character and faith. Sometimes I had to grin and bear waiting to get in the bathroom or just to cook in the kitchen. Most days I relied on God to use my spirit in good ways. So, I had to turn the other cheek often. But I wouldn't allow myself to complain, because I was not homeless, I had food in the refrigerator, and a safe place to lay my head. I could have had an ugly attitude, got into arguments about being 'right" but I just let God handle each situation for me. It wasn't the perfect situation, but I knew that God would work everything out for me.

One day at work, my boss asked me to come into the office, and at first I was shocked and a little fearful. Seeing that I had an intense stare on my face, he assured me I was fine, but that he wanted to offer me the opportunity to stay on in another capacity. I wasn't sure if that position was going to be permanent or what God had in store for me. On the last day of my employment as a volunteer, I had filled out paperwork for a position that would increase my quality of life. I accepted a full time position and was extremely grateful for God's favor. He blessed me in such a way that would never been forgotten and would be passed along to touch another's life. The angels were shouting a victory dance on my behalf as well as my colleagues and family.

It was God's grace that brought that amazing transformation in my life. One that I could never ever repay.

As things began to normalize in my life, God restored a lot of things. Members from my father's side of the family began appearing. I began trying to rebuild my family via social networks and communicated regularly with them. A huge contract was awarded to me from a former connection at a Chicago school where I had previously taught creative writing classes. I was now in a position where I could help family with some financial support, something I hadn't been able to do in many years. I got most of my bills on track and was even was able to pay some off within two months of starting my new position. God also blessed me with a better living arrangement in an area that was even closer to my employer's site and one where it was more peaceful and allowed me to rest.

I thought I was an independent woman, who could take care of myself. But the Lord humbled me and allowed me to see just how much I truly needed Him. Due to a lot of soul searching and nights alone with God on this journey in uncharted waters, He blessed me with volumes of love and light that moved mountains in my life. No need for replaying negative experiences in my mind, because that was the past, and God had lifted it off me so sweetly. Something awesome happens when you let go and let God have His way. God is then able to move powerfully in your mind, body, and spirit. The experience humbled me, especially when the real live angels, Mandy and her husband John, saved me from being homeless. That one act inspired me to continue to coast the waters and give God the reign to my life.

Pam Osbey is an author and radio host. She can be reached at www.facebook.com/pamosbey or by way of her blog radio show at: www.blogtalkradio.com/literarypizzazz

THE SHEILD OF FAITH
Michele Mills

*B*y faith Enoch was taken away so that he did not see death, *"and was not found, because God had taken him"*; before he was taken he had this testimony, that he pleased God. Hebrews 11:5 (NIV) Enoch walked with God, he had active fellowship with Him, and his commune was so intimate that God was pleased with him.

This enlightens us to believe that Enoch had a high degree of pleasure for God. He delighted himself in the Lord and God took great satisfaction in him. It was a two-way street. "Delight yourself also in the Lord, and He will give you the desires and secret petitions of your heart." (Psalm 37:4).

The more time we spend with Jesus, and the more we study and read His Word, the more his nature dominates our desire, meaning His desires become our desires. We become more driven to fulfill His will. Just like a husband and wife trying to find ways to please each other, because of the love that has grown within them for each other, and for that reason, the time spent together increases the desire, each begins to learn what pleases their mate.

When we delight ourselves in God and His will, God Himself places desires with in our hearts that He then sets out to fulfill. (Php 2:13)." Life in the Spirit Study Bible (NIV).

For instance, years ago, when God told me to quit my job, and open a childcare. I knew that this was God, simply because He had placed this desire in my heart for some time, and then it was time to act on it, step out on faith, and do what He had asked me to do. Therefore, I obtained my childcare license, prayed about a name, the cost and hours of operation. AAA Christian Family

Child Care came to mind, it stood for Andrea, Adrienne and Andre. It was my children's and my name. The childcare was low cost and had twenty-four hour service with transportation included. My children and I spent many days posting up Florissant pink flier, throughout Oakland in the area's that I had targeted. I started rearranging everything in my house, so that it could accommodate infants to school aged children. My business was flourishing. My mother, and two cousins were my assistant. My children would help me with outside and feeding times. It was such a blessing.

During this same time I had to step out on faith on another assignment, I was asked to be the Children's Director at my church, and the Youth Pastor, asked me to open a children's church. This was something that I had no experience in doing; it was definitely a leap of Faith. After much prayer and fasting, I agreed to do it, and then prayed about a name for the church. Noah's Ark Children's Church confirmed in my spirit. A core staff of eight people was formed. We met every Wednesday and began to plan for the success of the children's church. We used the same concept as Bill Winston, out of New York. He has one of the largest street ministries for children. His ministry teaches with object lessons, games, prizes, atmospheres of high energy for the children, the Holy Spirit was definitely in the midst of our ministry. After much prayer, planning, recruiting and practicing, it was finally time to launch Noah's Ark Children's Church. On Sunday's well over three hundred children attended, and on Tuesday Night's for "Jam for Jesus Night" well over a hundred and fifty children attended. It became a successful ministry; all built on an act of faith, the word of God, genuine love for each other and team work. Our slogan was "Team Work Makes the Dream Work," taken from John Maxwell leadership training/teaching. After a while, stepping out on faith became a lifestyle and the question would always arise, "Okay, Lord what is it that You would have me to do next?" Many times, people would not understand some of the things the Lord would test us to say, yes to. A prime example, after operating my childcare for five years, (2000-2005), the Lord said it was time to close and pursue full-time ministry, and to get prepared to start a women's ministry. Now mind you, I was making good money, well over seventy-five thousand a year. I even wanted to open a chain of childcare facilities. I acted on it and began to plan. I had a friend draw up the plans/vision for my next childcare center. I hung it upon the wall in my living room, so everyone could see the vision and run with it. However, it was not the Lord's desire or His will for my life. This goes to show, when we get in tune with God and His desires, He will let us know which way to go, even when our way feels right. Out of obedience and faith, I closed my childcare on August 1, 2005, and began the preparation for starting a women's ministry. The Lord started giving me dreams and desires for the women's ministry.

The color pink, butterflies and the word love, took residence in my spirit. After much prayer, fasting and Godly council, the name of the ministry was birthed. "Love Inspite of Women's Bible Fellowship and the logo was butterflies. Let me elaborate on the meaning, God has called us to love each other in spite of, meaning when we share our life, our pains, our struggles, or even our mistakes with each other, we are still expected to embrace each other.

A woman may share that she has been experiencing spousal abuse, and this treatment has caused her to abuse alcohol, in order to maintain the pain and shame, or another scenario can be two women having a disagreement and one is offended, do we still love and embrace each other the same as before, or do we keep a distance with a chip on our shoulder? The butterflies, represent the focus for our lives, after all the caterpillar days, and with the help of each other and the Lord's divine help, we are transformed into a beautiful butterfly and able to flow freely with the mind of Christ and genuine love toward one another; able to forgive and let go, able to pursue our God given purpose, able to reach for the stars. In other words, we are able to keep moving towards his destiny for our lives without bitterness.

After transformation, and developing a mind of Christ, the struggles and offenses will still come our way; however, we now are able to shake it off. Simply, because we know, and practice the word of God. "For we wrestle not against flesh and blood but against principalities, against powers, against the rulers of darkness of this world against spiritual wickedness in high places" Ephesians 6:12. Our enemy, the devil, will try all that he can to deter our faith in God and His word, He will try every tactic to cause havoc between individuals, that's blinded by Him.

Women need to be able to come together, and share, release and not feel ashamed the next day, but embraced by each other, so we can continue to walk this journey called life together by faith.

This type of faith has definitely become a process for me. I remember a time in my life when I did not think that I was going to make it. It appeared that everything around me had fallen apart. My faith was definitely on trial. It was a time when my mother needed help with her house, so she put my name on the mortgage in order to get a loan and hopefully get out of debt. Things looked good for a moment. The loan at the time seemed okay, especially the up front money, however, as time passed, I was laid off and didn't have the money to make the payments. So, we were approved for another loan to help us get out of the bind we were in, and again for a moment it appeared okay. The up front money looked good.

However, we were just digging ourselves into a deeper hole. Through these rough times, I still continued to pray and cry out to God, believing that He was going to come through and help us keep the house. On a daily basis, I comforted my mother and told her that everything was going to be alright and that God was in control. Despite our bad decision on taking the loan.

Well, a year passed by, and we finally had to give up the house. I could not believe it was truly happening. It came to the point where we were given the opportunity to "get cash for the keys". The realtor gave us three offers. The offer with the most money was the one asking us to leave within two-weeks, we passed on it. Actually, we passed on all, except the last offer. It gave us less money, but we took it because the contract allowed us to stay in the house another month. However, the realtor missed some important beats in the paperwork, so, we were able to stay for an additional month and receive more money. My mother and I saw that as a blessing.

Many people could not believe we were able to stay in foreclosure for over a year, before having to pick up everything and move. Through the entire process, I still believed God would show up supernaturally. I was under a supreme amount of pressure, still unemployed and my mother was trying to make ends meet with her retirement check.

Praise the Lord, my mother moved into a nice, newly remodeled one bedroom apartment and I moved my items into storage and put my clothes into the back seat of my van. Still thinking/believing that I was going to get a job to pay the storage. Soon after, my Windstar Van and my mother's Buick Regal both went out of commission at the same time. My church is about twenty-five miles away. So, I had to start riding the Bart train to Dublin and then walk the rest of the way to church. This really bothered me, but the Lord, supernaturally increased my faith to endure. As time went by, I had to do something I had never done in my life. I had to reach out to family, friends and my church for help. It was definitely a humbling experience. My church, the Well Christian Community Church blessed me in a way that brought tears to my eyes. I felt God's love in a way that I had never felt before. He was definitely doing a work in me. He showed me how to walk by faith without the spirit of pride. This experience showed me, that my mother and I were too prideful to ask for help, before it was too late. I've learned, no matter the outcome, reach out for help, even if the answer is no. We are called to be interdependent. The world teaches us to be independent. But, God has another way.

I ended up losing everything in storage, my family and children's pictures, wedding pictures, my large library of books, tapes, and DVDs. Lastly, I lost my ministerial certificates, awards and minister's license from different churches I labored in. This loss hit me hard. Until, one day in prayer, the Lord said, "Your storage is now empty." He revealed that He wanted me to let go of some things in my storage even though it was very painful. "But seek first his kingdom and his righteousness and all these things shall be given to you as well. Therefore do not worry about tomorrow, for tomorrow will worry about itself. Each day has enough trouble of its own," Matt 6:33:34

God was in it every step of the way. I have learned in this faith walk that God will allow us to lose things or people, as a test, to see if we will still love Him, in other words do we love the stuff more than we love Him.

He is a jealous God; He does not want us to put anything before Him, it could be our children, our family, our work, our money or even our house. He wants to be worshipped alone. God proved His love for us, when He gave His one and only son, Jesus Christ to die on the cross for each and every one of us. All the blood that Jesus shed before and on the cross was His great love for humanity.

This goes to show us that the Lord will allow and test us in losing things and people in order to get us to the next level in our faith walk and dependence on Him. I am a firm believer, no pain no gain. For example, after all the pain, all the ridicule, all the shame, all the rejection that Jesus experienced, He died and rose on the third day with all power in his hands. In other words, there's a cost to walk by faith. Just read the hall of faith....Hebrew 11.

"Now faith is the substance of things hoped for, the evidence of things not seen"

" By faith Noah, being warned of God of the things not seen as yet, moved with fear, prepared an ark to the saving of his house: by the which he condemned the world, and became heir of the righteousness which is by faith."

"By faith Abraham, when called to go to a place he would later receive as his inheritance, obeyed and went, even though he did not know where he was going. By faith he made his home in the promised land like a stranger in a foreign country; he lived in tents, as did Isaac and Jacob, who were heirs with him of the same promise. "Through faith also Sarah herself received strength to conceive seed, and was past age, because she judged him faithful who had promised." Hebrews 11: 8-11 (NIV,KJV)

Surprisingly, the experience and test of losing everything drew me closer to our Lord and Savior. It helped me take the value off of things and put more value on his presence and pleasing him.

Back in the day, this type of pressure would have caused me to start back drinking, just for some form of release. Simply because I used to believe this was a way of escape. This type of thinking was certainly a lie from the enemy, Satan himself. Nevertheless, I was deceived into thinking that drinking several glasses of Barcardi or Hennessey on the rocks would give me some release on the matter at hand.

Praise God, He has taught me when under pressure, the importance of walking by faith and not by sight, regardless, of what's going on, believe and know that it's ALL working together for the good. He has taught me to cast all of my cares on Him, for His yoke is easy and His burden is light. We must remember that Satan is our enemy and He will always try and magnify every situation. Most importantly, when the pressure appears to be unbearable, the Holy Spirit has taught me to use Peter as an example, when the turbulence of life tries to take us under, we can't look to the right, or the left, we have to keep our eyes fixed on Jesus, when Peter stepped out of the boat on faith and kept his eyes on Jesus, he was able to keep moving forward, but, when the storms and winds began to hit, he looked to the right and he looked to the left and began to sink. Praise the Lord; he's always there, to reach out and grab us.

By faith, we must put on the armor of God on a daily basis. By doing this every morning, it's a daily reminder of the battle at hand. Even though the battle isn't ours, but belongs to the Lord, it helps us be prepared to fight, so we are able to stand strong against the wiles of the devil. "Finally, my brethren, be strong in the Lord, and in the power of His might. Put on the whole Armor of God, that we may be able to stand against the wiles of the devil." Ephesians 6:10-11. Just a reminder of our Armor, which is our Helmet of salvation, our breastplate of righteousness, our sword of the spirit, our shield of faith, our belt of truth, and our shoes to spread the gospel. Therefore, we can be strong in the Lord and in the power of His might and He will increase our faith to stand in the midst of the storm.

Like Steven, he was a man that was full of faith. He was able to stand in the midst of the stoning. I can truly relate to the song by Marvin Sapp "Never Would Have Made It". I am stronger; I am wiser, I am so much better, because of the Lord.

He has also taught me the importance of being around strong believers, reading the word, prayer and going to church, when our faith is on trial.

Our supreme desire should be to have a testimony that we pleased God. Regardless of our plans, our struggles, the pleasures and even our most intense pressures, the ultimate focus should be to please God in all that we encounter. It should be the motivation that compels us daily. Our thoughts, our responses, and our decisions throughout life should be driven by the will of God Almighty. In other words it should be a lifestyle.

Enoch was diligent in seeking God and he was rewarded to the extent that he did not experience death. Just imagine by faith, you are walking with God, and He is so well-pleased with your efforts to live a holy life, and embrace His ways, that you walk right into the entrance of Heaven with Him, like Enoch. Oh what a sight to see!

The Lord Jesus Christ loves us immensely, and He is seeking such to have faith and believe that He is and that He is a rewarder of them that diligently seek Him(Hebrews 11:6). The good thing about it, as we seek Him, He is seeking too! It's a mutual relationship. He said draw nigh to me and I will draw nigh to you (James 4:8). When we step out on faith and walk with God, we are able to accomplish the impossible. Our nature becomes His nature, and His supernatural overtakes our natural. What great pleasure!

Here are some essentials to go with our shield of faith:

Meditate on the word..Joshua 1:8

Speak the word..John 6:63

Trust the word...Proverbs 3:5-6

Obey the word..John 14:15

Believe the word..James 1:6

Delight in the word..Psalm 37

Pray the word...1 John 5:14-15

Think the word...Philippians 4:8

"That's why I live with such good cheer. You won't see me drooping my head or dragging my feet! Cramped conditions on earth don't get me down. They only remind us of the spacious living conditions ahead. It's what I trust in, even though I don't yet see it… my faith keeps me going. A few ruts in the road or rocks in the path aren't going to stop me. When the time comes, I'll be plenty ready to exchange exile for homecoming." 2 Corinthians 5:7-8 (The Message)

Periodically, it becomes a fight to walk by faith using our shield of faith. As a result, it may appear at times, that it's about to be a TKO. However, we must keep fighting, keep pressing toward the mark for the prize. The Lord Jesus Christ is able to keep me and you from falling. "Now unto Him that is able to keep us from falling and present us faultless, before the present of His glory with exceeding joy, to the only wise God our savior be glory, majesty, dominion and power, both now and forever." Jude 2425.

"I have fought the good fight, I have finished the race, and I have kept the faith." 2 Timothy 4:7-8 (NKJV)

Andrea Mills is the Founder/CEO of Love Inspite of Women's Bible Fellowship, where Jesus Christ is Lord. Women's ministry leader and Bible teacher; her pen name is Michele Mills. Andrea is a published Christian author for varies books. She has two children and granddaughter.

For more information or to schedule for speaking engagement or book signing contact Michele_amills@yahoo.com.
www.loveinspiteofwomensbiblefellowship.com

Other Books in the Faith Anthology Series

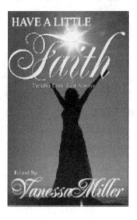

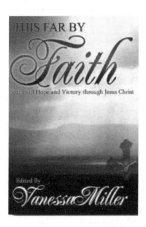

To order Have a Little Faith or This Far by Faith

Go to:

http://vanessamiller.com/books/faith-series/

About the editor

Vanessa Miller of Dayton, Ohio is a best-selling author, playwright, and motivational speaker. Her stage productions include: **Get You Some Business, Don't Turn Your Back on God,** and **Can't You Hear Them Crying.** Vanessa is currently in the process of turning the novels in the Rain Series into stage productions.

Vanessa has been writing since she was a young child. When she wasn't reading, writing poetry, short stories, stage plays and novels consumed her free time. However, it wasn't until she committed her life to the Lord in 1994 that she realized all gifts and anointing come from God. She then set out to write redemption stories that glorified God.

To date, Vanessa has written the Rain Series and the Storm Series. The books in the Rain Series are: **Former Rain, Abundant Rain,** and **Latter Rain**. The books in the Storm Series are: **Rain Storm** and **Through The Storm.** These books have received rave reviews, winning Best Christian Fiction Awards and topping numerous Bestseller's lists. Vanessa believes that each book in The Rain and Storm Series will touch readers across the country in a special way. It is, after all her God-given destiny to write and produce plays and novels that bring deliverance to God's people.

Vanessa is a dedicated Christian and devoted mother. She graduated from Capital University with a degree in Organizational Communication. In 2007 Vanessa was ordained by her church as an exhorter. Which of course, Vanessa believes was the right position for her because God has called her to exhort readers and to help them rediscover their place with the Lord.

Check out these other Books by Vanessa Miller

The Second Chance at Love Series

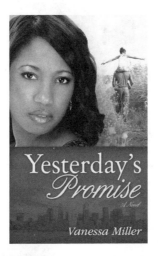

Purchase the Second Chance at Love Series at:

Bookstores Everywhere
Walmart
www.amazon.com
Black Expression Book Club
www.MochaReaders.com

Long Time Coming

Two women from different worlds find hope together.

Faithful Christian Deidre Clark-Morris is a professional career-minded woman with a loving husband, but no children. Kenisha Smalls has lived in poverty all her life. She has three children by three different men and has just been diagnosed with inoperable cervical cancer. While the meeting between these two women appears accidental, it becomes their catalyst of hope. Neither woman expects the blessing that God has in store for her. While Deidre will guide Kenisha on the path to eternal life with Jesus Christ, Kenisha will teach Deidre how to stand strong against the hard-knocks of life.

Purchase Long Time Coming at:

Bookstores Everywhere
Walmart
www.amazon.com
Black Expression Book Club
www.MochaReaders.com